D1368163

OPTICAL PROPERTIES OF MINERALS

A Determinative Table

OPTICAL
PROPERTIES OF
MINERALS

A DETERMINATIVE TABLE

By Horace Winchell
Department of Geology
Yale University
New Haven, Connecticut

1965

ACADEMIC PRESS   New York and London

549.1
W759o

ACADEMIC PRESS INC.
111 Fifth Avenue, New York, New York 10003

United Kingdom Edition published by
ACADEMIC PRESS INC. (LONDON) LTD.
Berkeley Square House, London W.1

LIBRARY OF CONGRESS CATALOG CARD NUMBER: 64-25684

PRINTED IN THE UNITED STATES OF AMERICA.

PREFACE

This book arose from the need for up-to-date data that would help to identify minerals optically without being too restrictive on the methods or the precision of measurements used for classification. The tabular format was developed along lines indicated in the Introduction, with helpful comments by several mineralogists and by several groups of students who contributed much by using and criticizing the preliminary drafts of the charts. Their experiences helped to improve both the content and the format of the charts.

There have been two periods of intensive revision, bringing information to update in each case by inserting the necessary addenda or by redrawing the charts; such insertions account for double entries in some index lists, for the lists must permit entry through both alphabetical and numerical references.

Most of the points were located and plotted in the diagrams by Jean H. Winchell, and the corresponding index lists were drawn up under her supervision. Without her careful work this table could not have been completed. Prof. J. V. Smith, editor of the X-ray Powder Data File, kindly gave permission on behalf of the American Society for Testing Materials to use data from the Index to the X-ray Powder Data File. The calculations for Fig. 3 and for the table accompanying it were performed on the IBM 1620 computer at the Yale Computer Center, with costs defrayed by the Higgins Fund for Fundamental Research.

Academic Press afforded outstanding editorial cooperation and deserves credit for great care in the preparation of difficult copy.

New Haven, Connecticut   HORACE WINCHELL
November 1964

CONTENTS

SUPPLEMENTARY INFORMATION

The following items should be added to complete the continuity of variation of certain minerals that vary within wide limits. The seven items followed by values (in parentheses) for $2V$ and B should be represented by new points to be plotted by the user.

Page	After the entry beginning	Insert
26	36 Minyulite	56 Montmorillonite 398
26	55 Tunellite	56 Montmorillonite 398 ($2V = -20, B = .022$)
30	25 Hannayite	25 Lepidolite 370
	31 Lembergite	25 Lepidolite 370
	42 Pyroaurite	42 Scapolite 352
	47 Saponite	42 Scapolite 352
34	19 Fremontite	31 Glauconite 378
	31 Lepidolite	31 Glauconite 378
38	2 Aminoffite	5 Andalusite 521
	4 APATITE	4 Chlorite 384
	5 Arrojadite	5 Andalusite 521
	7 Bementite	7 Glauconite 378
	13 Childrenite	4 Chlorite 384
	15 Clinoenstatite	46 Clinohumite 515
	23 Ferrocarpholite	7 Glauconite 378
	46 Olivine	46 Clinohumite 515
40	31 Hinsdalite	71 Hornblende 435
	70 Witherite	71 HORNBLENDE 435 ($2V = -66, B = .022$)
42	7 Axinite	7 Hypersthene 405
	18 Harstigite	⎰ 44 Hornblende 435 ⎱ 7 Hypersthene 405
	43 Cenosite	44 HORNBLENDE 435 ($2V = -38, B = .020$)
44	5 Barylite	5 Hypersthene 405
	18 HORNBLENDE	5 Hypersthene 405
46	9 Donbassite	51 Epidote 449
	50 Innelite	51 EPIDOTE 449 ($2V = -85, B = .023$)
48	1 Caryocerite	1 GARNET GROUP 483
	9 CHRYSOBERYL	⎰ 2 Epidote 449 ⎱ 34 Ferrohypersthene 406
	10 Freirinite	1 Garnet group 483
	33 Wolfeite	34 Ferrohypersthene 406 ($2V = -65, B = .018$)
50	Isotropic	1 GARNET GROUP 483
	4 Allanite	4 Scorodite 185
	18 Ferrohypersthene	1 Garnet group 483
	32 Sahamalite	4 Scorodite 185
52	18 Olivenite	⎰ 29 Olivine 498 ⎱ 30 Pseudomalachite 229
	28 Stishovite	⎰ 29 Olivine 498 ($2V = -75, B = .045$) ⎱ 30 Pseudomalachite 229 ($2V = -46, B = .08$)
	1 Berzeliite	1 GARNET GROUP 483
	13 Gadolinite	1 Garnet group 483

INTRODUCTION

General Statement

The suggestion that optical properties be used as the basis of determinative tables and charts for minerals is probably as old as the techniques for measuring them. Various different tabular arrangements have been tried, of which perhaps the most widely used in most modern tables places the minerals in the order of increasing values of an arbitrarily chosen classificatory index n_y or n_0 or n. The tables of Larsen (1921) and of Larsen and Berman (1934) consist of five main sections, respectively for isotropic, uniaxial positive, uniaxial negative, biaxial positive, and biaxial negative minerals. Although multiple entries have partially solved the problem of variable properties and overlap due to substitution of various elements for one another, these tables do not represent the most convenient and versatile arrangement possible.

Previous Tables for the Optical Determination of Minerals

The tables of A. N. Winchell (1939), evolved from an earlier edition of 1909, present all the essential refringence data in a single sequence indicating optic sign by setting entries to the right or to the left of center in the column reserved for the classificatory index n, n_0, or n_y, and correctly treating isotropic and uniaxial minerals as special cases of the more general biaxial type. The unique feature of Winchell's tables is the explicit indication of variability by means of vertical lines in the left margin of the table, extending continuously from the entry of lowest index to that of highest index for each mineral species. Thus, the searcher is led not only to the names listed in the immediate vicinity of the index he observed on an unknown mineral; by these vertical lines he also finds the minerals whose index n_y or n_0 or n may vary so as to include that of his unknown.

Two-Dimensional Classifications of Mineral Optics

Winchell (1939), Troeger (1952, 1956, 1959), and others, have presented optical determinative charts based on n_y plotted as abscissa of

1

a graph and $B = (n_z - n_x)$ as ordinate, positive (upward) for positive minerals and negative (downward) for negative ones (Fig. 1A). The artificiality of this arrangement is apparent in the case of plagioclase, which jumps discontinuously from positive to negative ordinates as $2V$ varies continuously through 90°. Uniaxial minerals are not distinguished on such charts; isotropic ones appear along the central axis of abscissas.

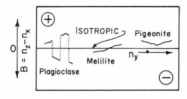

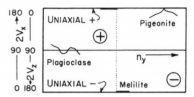

Fig. 1A. Graph of birefringence and refringence.

Fig. 1B. Graph of optic angle and refringence.

An alternate arrangement that corrects the feldspar-type difficulty is to plot $2V_z$ downward along the ordinate-axis from 0° to 180°, as in Fig. 1B. ($2V_x$ also then runs from 0° to 180° along the same scale, but in opposite direction.) This arrangement places uniaxial positive minerals along the upper boundary, neutral minerals ($2V = 90°$) along the central axis between positive and negative fields, and uniaxial negative ones along the lower boundary. However, it is possible for uniaxial minerals such as melilite and idocrase to vary through zero birefringence and thus to change sign, requiring discontinuous variation curves in this case also. Unlike Fig. 1A, this chart fails to provide any position for isotropic substances.

Another arrangement with some merit uses another function for the ordinate, namely the difference between the two principal partial birefringences,

$$(n_z - n_y) - (n_y - n_x) = n_z + n_x - 2n_y.$$

The scheme is diagrammed in Fig. 1C. The number $n_z + n_x - 2n_y$ varies in most respects like $(n_z - n_x) \times \cos(2V_z)$, which could also be used as ordinate. These two possibilities have not been exploited, so far as I know. They would produce some curious associations, for two minerals with similar values of n_y would have the same position in the diagram if, for example, one has low total birefringence

2

$n_z - n_x$ with any value of $2V$, and the other has $2V$ near 90°, with any value of $n_z - n_x$.

Evidently all two-dimensional projections of an inherently three-dimensional system will have disadvantages.

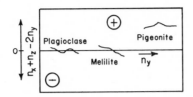

Fig. 1C. Graph of $(n_z + n_x - 2n_y)$ and refringence.

Three-Dimensional Arrangements

An obvious suggestion for a three-dimensional graph would be to plot the three principal refractive indices n_x, n_y, n_z along the axes XYZ of a Cartesian cordinate system as in Fig. 1D. The resulting field, however, is limited and somewhat unsymmetrical because

$$1.0 \leq n_x \leq n_y \leq n_z,$$

and $n_z - n_x$ is rarely greater than 0.2. Surfaces of constant value for the refractive index n_y would be planes parallel to the axes of n_x and n_z, one of which is shown in Fig. 1D and reproduced without projective distortion in Fig. 1E. Surfaces of constant birefringence in Fig. 1D are planes parallel to the axis of n_y and at 45° to those of n_z and

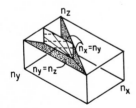

Fig. 1D. Three dimensional graph of refractive indices n_x, n_y, and n_z in rectangular coordinates.

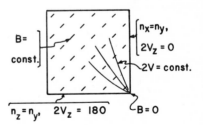

Fig. 1E. Detail of Fig. 1D.

n_x; they intersect the section shown in Fig. 1E along the dashed lines. Surfaces of constant value for the optic axial angle $2V_z$ (or $2V_x$) are curved; they pass through the locus of isotropic behavior

3

$(n_x = n_y = n_z)$ which is the body-diagonal through the origin of the cube in Fig. 1D, and intersect the section shown in Fig. 1E along the (solid) diagonal curves. For combinations of refractive indices appropriate to minerals the curvature is small, but not negligible.

Preferred Three-Dimensional Chart

A better scheme, rather simply related to this, is to use a hemi-cylindrical field (Fig. 1F) with the classificatory principal refractive index (n, n_0, or n_y) along the axis of the cylinder; $2V_z$ is used as

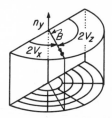

Fig. 1F. Hemi-cylindrical coordinate field for n_y, $2V$, and B.

azimuth angle defining a plane that contains the cylinder axis, and $B = n_z - n_x$ is represented by radial distance from that axis. Figures 1A–1C are special projections of this hemi-cylinder, and the small useful field between the dotted planes in Fig. 1D becomes the whole of the space defined by the hemi-cylindrical coordinates (Winchell, 1958).

In such a three-dimensional solid "diagram," an isotropic substance lies on the central axis of the hemi-cylinder at a point determined solely by its refractive index n. Uniaxial substances lie on the axial boundary plane of the hemi-cylinder, positive uniaxial ones on one side, and negative ones on the other side of the central axis, and distant from that axis by amounts varying only with the total birefringence. So far this is very like the scheme in Fig. 1A, but the third dimension of the hemi-cylinder is required to show the relations for biaxial substances. The cylindrical coordinate field has the following special advantages. There is a unique place for every substance, and unlike substances fall near one another only if there is some possibility that microscopic determination of their optical properties may lead to confusion. Thus it is notably difficult to determine optic sign of minerals that have $2V$ near $90°$, but other properties such as n_y, B,

4

and the fact that $2V$ *is* large, may be estimated or determined readily in thin section or immersion, and there would be no difficulty because all substances with "large" $2V$ are fairly close to the plane locus corresponding to $2V = 90°$ in the hemi-cylinder. In another instance (for example, some chlorite specimens) the birefringence is very low, and it may be exceedingly difficult to determine either the sign or a value for $2V$. Such ambiguity is not significant because all such substances lie close to the cylinder axis.

Identification by Thin-Section Study

By using the thickness of a section and the numerical aperture of the objective, the student of thin sections can, from a single grain giving a well-centered optic-axis interference figure, estimate all the quantities necessary to locate approximately the part of the hemi-cylindrical coordinate space in which his mineral must lie. He can obtain by direct examination of such an interference figure a good idea of $2V$. An accessory plate will help to determine the sign in all but ambiguous cases where $2V$ is nearly 90°. Thickness of the section, and interference color at the *edge* of the interference figure, together with the value of the numerical aperture and a rough estimate of refractive index from relief, yield the birefringence (see page 00); this is perhaps the least familiar possibility to most petrographers. It is only moderately accurate, but if a second grain with flash-figure orientation can be located in the same thin section, the birefringence can be estimated with considerable precision. The original optic-axis grain yields by its relief an estimate of the refractive index n_0 or n_y, through which the axial coordinate of the cylindrical space is established.

A practical development of the hemi-cylindrical coordinate field on pages of convenient size is shown in the subsequent figures herewith. Each projection on the cylinder-base shows all points falling within a "slice" between arbitrarily chosen levels of n_y. These levels are spaced so that relief in thin section can be used to estimate n_y within limits of not more than two or three adjacent "slices" of the cylinder; birefringence and optic angle can both be estimated from an interference figure as noted above.

Thus the position of a mineral in these coordinates can be found by thin-section study, and therefore the mineral can be identified.

Identification by the Immersion Method

The values of n_y, B, and $2V$ are likewise obtainable from grains of the crushed powder of the mineral by using a series of calibrated refractive-index liquids, using conventional, or more precise immersion methods.

Finding Minerals in the Charts

Each "slice" of the hemi-cylinder has serially numbered points, and a key to these numbers on the facing page permits finding mineral names either by number or by alphabetical position. Many substances are entered twice, once so that their names are in alphabetical position and once in numerical position. Thus entries that are out of place numerically are in alphabetical position and vice versa. Importance of minerals is indicated approximately by the type: VERY COMMON, Ordinary, and *Rare*. Minerals that vary rather widely in properties are entered as many times as seemed necessary to ensure the user's convenience in finding them. For example, olivine is to be found on every chart from 1.64 to 1.85; obviously the user must consult more detailed data to determine the composition of an olivine. Such consultation is made convenient by page references to Winchell and Winchell (1951), or to the literature in the case of minerals more recently described. Following the page reference are given in parentheses the spacings ("d") for the three or more strongest lines of the X-ray powder pattern, and the card number, if any, in the 1960 edition of the Index to the X-ray Powder Data File, published by the American Soceity for Testing Materials. These X-ray data are often sufficient to eliminate from consideration some minerals that would be possible on the basis of optical data alone; their presence indicates availability of the powder pattern. Agreement with observed spacings should be considered necessary but not sufficient evidence to confirm an identification. Minerals for which more than one pattern is given in the X-ray Powder Data File are so indicated by an asterisk after the serial number.

Coverage of the Present Tables

Although it would be impossible to obtain perfect coverage for all minerals and for all time, it has been found practicable to cover all mentioned in the comprehensive standard reference books cited in the bibliography, and in addition to cover all that have been cited or described in *Mineralogical Abstracts* (abbreviated MA), Vols. 11-15 (No. 6) through mid-1962, and ones cited or described in *American Mineralogist* (abbreviated AM) through Vol. 47 (No. 6), dated May-June, 1962 or in *Mineralogical Magazine* (abbreviated MM) through Vol. 33 (No. 257), dated June, 1962. It is hoped that this later coverage will serve a useful purpose. Some new minerals mentioned in these references had to be omitted for lack of sufficient optical data.

PROCEDURES FOR PRACTICAL USE OF THE TABLE

General Statement

There cannot be any single fixed procedure in the intelligent use of physical properties so varied, and in connection with specimens that assume so many different forms, as will be found among minerals. The following discussion cannot therefore replace an at least elementary understanding of the principles and practice of mineralogical and petrographic microscopy as set forth in standard works such as Winchell (1951), Hartshorne and Stuart (1960), Bloss (1961). Certain important, but less generally emphasized methods will be described here.

Preparation of Material: Powders

The initial condition and amount of any specimen naturally affect the nature of the tests to be used. If abundant material is available, the immersion method will usually, and most quickly, give the greatest information, consisting of at least the three principal refractive indices n_x, n_y, n_z, the least index n_x, for light vibrating parallel to X; the intermidiate index n_y, for light vibrating parallel to Y (which is normal to the plane containing the vibration directions X and Z); and the greatest index n_z, for light vibrating parallel to Z. The optic axial angle $2V$, expressed as $2V_z$ if the mineral is optically positive, $2V_x$ if negative, should be estimated by means of interference figures or rotation devices; even if such an estimate may be accurate only to the nearest 10 or 15°, especially if the birefringence $n_z - n_x$ is low, it yet may be better than the value that can be calculated from refractive indices that have been measured only to the nearest 0.001. The birefringence B is $n_z - n_x$. It should be estimated from interference colors (or other measurement of retardation using a Berek compensator or similar instrument) only in thin sections because the accuracy of this measurement is proportional to the precision with which the grain thickness can be determined, and that in turn is rarely measureable in irregular grains of powder.

The use of a gelatin-coated slide for mounting a few grains so as to permit examination of one and the same grain in several calibrated index-liquids (Vedeneeva and Melancholin, 1932; Fairbairn, 1943) is especially recommended if little material is available. In some cases, manipulation with a needle while the adhesive gelatin is still soft may permit placing fibrous grains or thin cleavage flakes upright.

A spindle-stage (Wilcox, 1959) providing controlled rotation of a single grain about an axis parallel to the microscope stage permits the adjustment of the grain at will so as to transmit light vibrating parallel to each of the vibration directions X, Y, and Z of the grain. This grain may be immersed successively in different index liquids. The principal indices n_x, n_y, n_z are thus unequivocably determinable from a single grain cemented in a random orientation to the tip of a pointed spindle. Although first proposed as an aid in universal stage work, the spindle-stage alone, mounted on the ordinary stage of the microscope, is sufficient for precise refractive index measurement.

By varying temperature and/or wavelength of light, during the study of a grain, the precision of measurement of refractive indices can be improved considerably. Emmons (1928, p. 504; 1931, p. 553) shows that the precision is certainly better than $\pm$ 0.001, and under some conditions it is as good as $\pm$ 0.0002. Combining such double-variation methods with the spindle stage (Fisher, 1962) promises great improvement in the art of refractive index measurement under the polarizing microscope, and at very nominal cost in added time and equipment. Spindle-stage settings probably meet even rather extreme orientation requirements (Gillberg, 1960) for precise measurement of refractive index, because interference figures can be used.

Thin Sections

Many experienced petrographers and optical mineralogists do not take full advantage of all the possibilities available to obtain numerical optical data from thin sections. That a petrographic study can identify anything at all in covered thin sections is remarkable; that

8

we usually can not only identify the mineral phases present but also estimate their chemical composition is even more so. The usual petrographic study depends mainly upon extinction angles, which in turn depend upon the crystallographic orientation of the section and the optic orientation, or orientation of the indicatrix axes X, Y, and Z with respect to crystallographic axes a, b, and c. However, certain numerical estimates are possible too.

Refractive Index

The relief of a mineral in thin section can be used to estimate its refractive index within limits that increase somewhat with increasing difference between index of mineral and index of surrounding medium (be it the mounting cement or another mineral). Nevertheless, by using not only the known index of the cement, but also those of associated minerals, an estimate of relief can usually give the value of refractive index within reasonable working limits. The uniform (and measureable) thickness of the section enables the petrographer to measure birefringence easily, by using measurements of retardation (made either by comparison of interference colors with those in Michel-Levy's birefringence chart, or by more precise compensator methods) and optic orientation in the well-known equation,

$$R = B't' = (B \times \sin \theta' \times \sin \theta'') \times (t/\cos \rho)$$

where R = retardation, B' = birefringence in the direction of observation, at an angle θ' to one optic axis and θ'' to the other, $B = n_z - n_x$ the total birefringence, and t' = distance the light travels through the crystal, usually the same as the section thickness t, but more accurately $t/\cos \rho$, where ρ is the angle between the light rays and the normal to the section.

Measuring 2V in Thin Sections and Grains

One or more grains may be examined in thin section or in immersion oils, and if $2V$ is small enough a fairly accurate measurement of $2V$ may be obtained by measuring the distance between the melatopes ("eyes," or points of emergence of the optic axes) in the interference figure obtained with grains approximately normal to the acute bisectrix. The formula for this determination is

$$2V = \arcsin\left(\frac{\text{N.A.}}{n_y} \times \frac{\text{separation of melatopes}}{\text{diameter of field}}\right)$$

9

where N. A. is the numerical aperture of the objective, n_y is the intermediate principal refractive index (which usually may be estimated accurately enough from the relative relief of the mineral in the thin section), and the separation and diameter are measured in any arbitrary units such as those of a scale in the focal plane of the ocular. A convenient chart for this calculation is presented in Fig. 2 (Win-

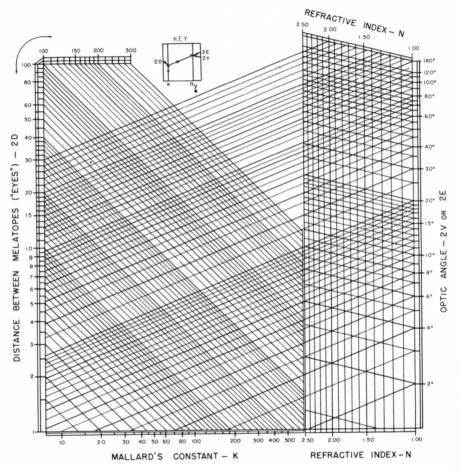

Fig. 2. Chart of $2D/2 = K \sin (2E/2) = n_y K \sin (2V/2)$. Measurement of optical axial angle from acute bisectrix interference figure.

(1) Calibrate chart by drawing a vertical line through Mallard's constant, K, for combination of ocular and objective to be used, or through intersection of lines representing $2D$ and $2E$ as obtained for an oriented section of a mineral of known optic angle.

(2) Measure $2D$ in interference figure of unknown.

(3) Follow lines as shown in key.

10

chell, 1946). This chart must be calibrated by measuring the separation ($2D$) of the melatopes in an interference figure produced by a substance of known $2E$ (or $2V$ and n_y), and drawing a vertical line through the corresponding point in the body of the chart, thus determining K for the lens system and micrometer scale in use.

Measuring $2V$, n_y, and B by Means of Observations on a Single Grain in Thin Section

An accurately centered optic-axis interference figure may be used to estimate $2V$ by a method suggested by Wright (1905, 1907). This depends upon the measurement of the curvature of the isogyre passing through the center of the field of view when the stage is rotated 45° from the position at which the isogyre is aligned with the crosshairs. Wright's theoretical treatment of isogyres has been re-studied by Kamb, who developed a new equation for the position of the isogyre (Kamb, 1958; especially equation 38). Although Kamb's conclusion is that Wright's original diagram is essentially correct,

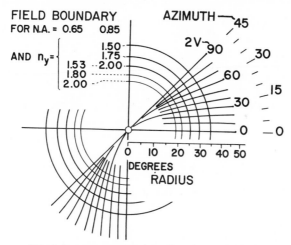

Fig. 3. Isogyre curvature in optic-axis inteference figures.

the new equation has been applied to recalculate the diagram, as shown in Fig. 3. In Fig. 3, several circles represent the relative positions of the edge of the field of view for the two commonly used objectives, N. A. = 0.85 and N. A. = 0.65, and for several values of n_y. The scale of degrees corresponds to declination of the rays of light from vertical (i.e., the angle between the wave-normal of the ray inside the crystal and the axis of the conoscopic lens-system). The curves representing positions of the isogyre are based upon positions calculated by Kamb's equation 38 at 5° intervals of declination, and are valid to declination 50°. Note that the azimuth reading for the point where the isogyre cuts the field boundary, and for an effective aperture-radius of 35°, is practically equal to the value of V.

The preceding paragraph assumes a knowledge of n_y in estimating the value of $2V$ from the optic-axis intereference figure. For this purpose n_y need not be known accurately. It can be obtained by estimate based upon the relief of the grain relative to known grains in the same mounting medium, or it may have been obtained by the direct measurement in immersion liquids.

Birefringence Estimate from Optic-Axis Interference Figures

The third variable, birefringence $(B = n_z - n_x)$, can be estimated in the same optic-axis interference figure by observing the retardation (i.e., interference color) at the edge of the field on the concave side of the isogyre in the 45° position; the partial birefringence B' in that direction is related to the total birefringence $B = n_z - n_x$ by the relation $B' = B(\sin \theta')(\sin \theta'')$, where θ' and θ'' are the angles between the direction concerned (here, the edge of the field at a point as far as possible from both optic axes), and the two respective optic axes. In the case of a uniaxial crystal, this equation simplifies to $B' = B(\sin^2 \theta)$. For practical situations, Fig. 3 shows that one of these angles, say θ' is the angular radius of the field of the interference figure, generally 25° to 35° depending upon n_y for a conoscopic objective with N. A. = 0.85, or 19° to 25° depending upon n_y if the aperture of the objective is only 0.65. A correction for thickness of section in oblique directions will be required, namely $t' = t/(\cos \rho)$, where t' is the inclined path-distance and t is the true thickness of the section, and ρ is the angle between the ray and the normal to the section. In the present case, $\rho = \theta'$. The other optic axis is inclined at $2V$ degrees from the first (vertical) one, and this gives immediately for the conditions assumed,

$$\theta'' = \theta' + 2V.$$

Hence the greatest retardation R at the margin of the interference figure as described is

$$R = B't' = B \times (\sin \theta') \times (\sin \theta'') \times \frac{t}{\cos \theta'}.$$

12

Explicitly, the true birefringence is therefore

$$B = (R/t) \times (\cot \theta') \times [\csc(2V + \theta')] = (R/t) \times (K)$$

where R is the observed greatest retardation at the margin of the optic-axis interference figure, t is the true thickness of the section, and θ' is the angular radius at the margin (from Fig. 3). The trigonometric portion K of this expression is given for various values of θ' and $2V$ in Table 1, which applies for uniaxial as well as biaxial optic axis interference figures.

TABLE 1. DATA FOR ESTIMATING BIREFRINGENCE, B, FROM RETARDATION, R, AT THE EDGE OF AN OPTIC AXIS INTERFERENCE FIGURE, USING $B = (R/t)(K)$

Table of $K = (\cot \rho)[\csc(2V + \rho)]$

2V	Angular radius, ρ, of interference figure field						
	20	25	30	35	40	45	50
0	8.033	5.074	3.464	2.490	1.854	1.414	1.095
5	6.501	4.289	3.020	2.222	1.685	1.305	1.024
10	5.495	3.739	2.695	2.020	1.556	1.221	0.969
15	4.790	3.336	2.449	1.864	1.455	1.155	0.926
20	4.274	3.033	2.261	1.743	1.376	1.103	0.893
25	3.886	2.799	2.114	1.649	1.315	1.064	0.869
30	3.587	2.618	2.000	1.576	1.268	1.035	0.852
35	3.354	2.476	1.911	1.520	1.234	1.015	0.842
40	3.173	2.366	1.843	1.479	1.210	1.004	0.839
45	3.032	2.282	1.793	1.450	1.196	1.000	0.842
50	2.924	2.220	1.759	1.434	1.192	1.004	0.852
55	2.844	2.178	1.739	1.428	1.196	1.015	0.869
60	2.790	2.153	1.732	1.434	1.210	1.035	0.893
65	2.758	2.145	1.739	1.450	1.234	1.064	0.926
70	2.747	2.153	1.759	1.479	1.268	1.103	0.969
75	2.758	2.178	1.793	1.520	1.315	1.155	1.024
80	2.790	2.220	1.843	1.576	1.376	1.221	1.095
85	2.844	2.282	1.911	1.649	1.455	1.305	1.187
90	2.924	2.366	2.000	1.743	1.556	1.414	1.305
95	3.032	2.476	2.114	1.864	1.685	1.556	1.463
100	3.173	2.618	2.261	2.020	1.854	1.743	1.678

In various countries different sets of symbols are in use for optical properties. The universally recognized symbol n stands for refractive index, and a subscript is a convenient means to indicate the vibration direction concerned. The principal vibration directions X, Y, Z are occasionally named by the German Script letters 𝔞, 𝔟, 𝔠, the corresponding Gothic letters 𝖆, 𝖇, 𝖈, or the Greek letters α, β, γ. In treatments using tensor notation, these vibration directions are also called X_1, X_2, X_3, (collectively X_i), and the principal refractive indices

13

are n_i; but frequently n_1 and n_2 are the lower and higher indices observed in random orientations: $n_x \leq n_1 \leq n_y \leq n_2 \leq n_z$.

In uniaxial crystals the ordinary ray O vibrates at right angles to the optic axis and the extraordinary ray E, parallel to it. The symbols for the indices then use these letters or their Greek equivalents (ω, ϵ), but occasionally their relation to biaxial crystals is emphasized by designating the ordinary index n_y or equivalent, and the extraordinary index n_x if the crystal is optically negative, n_z if positive.

Biaxial	n_x	α	N_p	n_α	n_1
	n_y	β	N_m	n_β	n_2 collectively n_i
	n_z	γ	N_g	n_γ	n_3
Uniaxial	n_o	ω	N_O	n_ω	
	n_e	ϵ	N_E	n_ϵ	
Isotropic	n	n	N	n	n

REFERENCES

Bloss, F. D. (1961). "An Introduction to the Methods of Optical Crystallography." Holt, Rinehart, and Winston, New York, pp. 1-294.

Emmons, R. C. (1928). The double dispersion method of mineral determination. *Am. Mineral.* **13**, 504-515.

Emmons, R. C. (1931), Additional comments on the double variation apparatus. *Am. Mineral.* **16**, 552-555.

Emmons, R. C. (1942). The Universal Stage. *Geol. Soc. Am., Mem.* **8**, 1-206.

Fairbairn, H. W. (1943). Gelatin-coated slides for refractive index immersion mounts. *Am. Mineral.* **28**, 396-397.

Fisher, D. J. (1962). Temperature control spindle stage. *Am. Mineral.* **47**, 649-664.

Gillberg, M. (1960). The error caused by inexact orientation in the determination of refractive indices by the immersion method. *Ark. Mineral. Geol.* **2** (38), 509-518.

Hartshorne, N. H., and Stuart, A. (1960). "Crystals and the Polarizing Microscope," 3rd ed. Arnold, London.

Johannsen, A. (1918). "Manual of Petrographic Methods." McGraw-Hill, New York.

Kamb, W. B. (1958). Isogyres in interference figures. *Am. Mineral.* **43**, 1029.

Larsen, E. S., Jr. (1921). "The Microscopic Determination of the Nonopaque Minerals," U. S. Geol. Survey Bull. **679**, (1st ed.) U. S. Government Printing Office, Washington, D. C., pp. 1-294.

Larsen, E. S., Jr. and Berman, H. (1934). *Ibid.*, Bull. **848** (2nd ed.), pp. 1-266.

Troeger, W. E. (1952). "Tabellen zur optischen Bestimmung der gesteinsbildenden Minerale." E. Schweitzerbart'sche Verlag., Stuttgart, pp. 1-147.

Troeger, W. E. (1956). *Ibid.*, 2nd ed., pp. 1-147.

Troeger, W. E. (1959), *Ibid.*, 3rd ed., pp. 1-147.

Vedeneeva, N. and Melancholin, N. (1932). The theodolite immersion method, etc., *Trans. Sci. Invest. Inst. Ind.* No. **503**; *Inst. App. Mineral., Paper* **54** (Russian and English). (From Fairbairn, 1943.)

Wilcox, R. E. (1959). Use of spindle stage for determining refractive indices of crystal fragments. *Am. Mineral.* **44**, 1272-1293.

Winchell, A. N. (1937). "Elements of Optical Mineralogy, Part I, Principles and Methods." Wiley, New York, pp. 1-263.

Winchell, A. N. (1939). "Elements of Optical Mineralogy, Part III, Determinative tables." Wiley, New York, 2nd ed., 2nd printing, pp. 1–231.

Winchell, A. N., and Winchell, Horace (1951). "Elements of Optical Mineralogy, Part II, Descriptions of minerals." Wiley, New York, pp. 1–551.

Winchell, Horace (1946). A chart for measurement of interference figures. *Am. Mineral.* **31,** 43–50.

Winchell, Horace (1958). New determinative table based on optical properties. (Abstract.) *Geol. Soc. Am., Bull.* **69,** 1664.

Wright, F. E. (1905). The determination of the optical character of birefracting minerals. *Am. Jour. Sci.* **20,** 285.

Wright, F. E. (1907). The measurement of the optic axial angle of minerals in the thin section. *Am. Jour. Sci.* **24,** 317.

Isotropic

1 *Carobbiite* [Strunz 1956, MA 13 382] (d 2.32, 1.64, 1.34; 4-0793)
1 *Cryolithionite* 33 (d 1.96, 4.28, 2.21; 2-1282)
1 *Cryptohalite* 35 (d 4.84, 2.42, 2.10; 7-13)
1 *Elpasolite* 35 (d 2.86, 2.02, 2.34; 8-70)
1 *Hieratite* 35 (d 4.70, 2.35, 2.88; 7-217)
1 *Neighborite* [Chao *et al.* 1961, AM 46 379–393; MA 15 459] (d 1.919, 2.715, 3.838)
1 *Ralstonite* 36 (d 5.71, 3.00, 2.87; 8-67)
1 *Villiaumite* 25 (d 2.32, 1.64, 1.34; 4-0793)

Anisotropic and isotropic

1 *Avogadrite* 36 (d 3.64, 2.19, 2.57; 3-0333*)
1 *Carobbiite* [Strunz 1956, MA 13 382] (d 2.32, 1.64, 1.34; 4-0793)
2 *Chiolite* 33 (d 2.90, 5.17, 2.32; 2-0749)
1 Cryolite 35 (d 1.94, 2.76, 2.33; 8-73*)
1 *Cryolithionite* 33 (d 1.96, 4.28, 2.21; 2-1282)
1 *Cryptohalite* 35 (d 4.84, 3.42, 2.10; 7-13)
1 *Elpasolite* 35 (d 2.86, 2.02, 2.34; 8-70*)
3 *Ferruccite* 36
1 *Hieratite* 35 (d 4.70, 2.35, 2.88; 7-217)
1 ICE 57 (d 3.68, 2.07, 3.45; 1-0509*)
4 *Malladrite* 36 (2.29, 1.80, 3.34; 8-36)
5 Mirabilite 170 (5.50, 3.22, 3.10; 1-0207), weberite 34 (1.78, 2.96, 2.90; 5-0733*)
1 *Neighborite* [Chao *et al.* 1961, AM 46 379–393; MA 15 459] (d 1.919, 2.715, 3.838)
1 *Ralstonite* 36 (d 5.71, 3.00, 2.87; 8-67)
6 *Sellaite* 29 (d 3.27, 2.23, 1.71; 6-0290)
1 *Villiaumite* 25 (d 2.32, 1.64, 1.34; 4-0793)
5 *Weberite* 34 (d 1.78, 2.96, 2.90; 5-0733*)

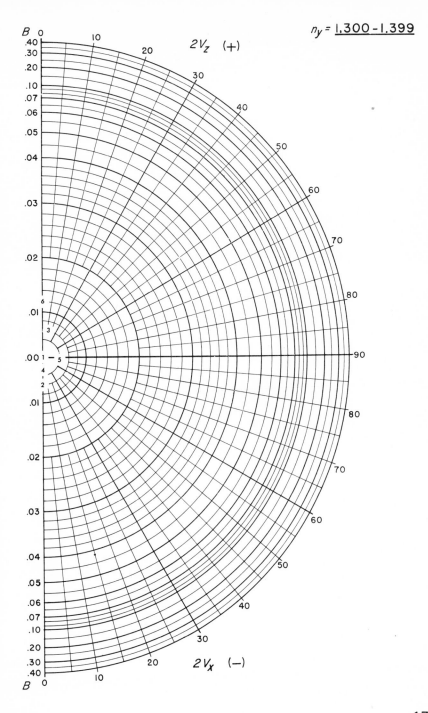

$n_y = \underline{1.300 - 1.399}$

$2V_z$ (+)

$2V_x$ (−)

17

1.400–1.459

Isotropic
1 *Chukhrovite* [Ermilova *et al.* 1960, MA 15 292] (d 2.193, 1.834, 3.261, 2.572, 2.294)
1 FLUORITE 27 (d 1.93, 3.15, 1.65; 4-0864)
1 *Hieratite* 35 (d 4.70, 2.35, 2.88; 7-217)
1 Lechatelierite 250 (amorphous)
1 Opal 251
1 Potassalumite (= K-alum) 154 (d 4.30, 3.25, 4.05; 7-17)
1 *Ralstonite* 36 (d 5.71, 3.00, 2.87; 8-67)
1 *Sulfohalite* 174 (d 3.56, 2.91, 1.76; 3-0345)
1 *Tschermigite* (NH_4-alum) 154 (d 4.33, 4.08, 3.27; 7-22)

Anisotropic and isotropic
2 *Cryptohalite* 35 (d 4.84, 2.42, 2.10; 7-13)
3 EPSOMITE 155 (d 4.21, 5.35, 2.68; 8-467), kalinite 154
4 *Erionite* 337
1 FLUORITE 27 (d 1.93, 3.15, 1.65; 4-0864)
5 *Galeite* [Pabst *et al.* 1955, MA 13 86]
6 *Gearksutite* 37 (d 4.55, 3.15, 2.28; 5-0283), *thomsenolite* 36 (d 4.02, 1.96, 2.00, 5-0343)

7 *Hexahydrite* 158 (d 4.40, 2.92, 4.04; 1-0354)
1 *Hieratite* 35 (d 4.70, 2.35, 2.88; 7-217)
8 *Jarlite* 37 (d 2.98, 3.19, 2.15; 5-0594)
3 *Kalinite* 154
1 Lechatelierite 250
9 Lecontite 170 (d 5.07, 4.65, 4.37; 5-0242*)
10 *Mendozite* 160
11 *Mercallite* 169
12 Natron 126 (d 5.50, 3.22, 3.10; 1-0207)
1 Opal 251
13 *Pachnolite* 36 (d 3.95, 1.97, 2.79; 5-0356)
1 Potassalumite (= K-alum) 154 (d 4.30, 3.25, 4.05; 7-17)
1 *Ralstonite* 36 (d 5.71, 3.00, 2.87; 8-67)
14 *Sassolite* 78 (d 3.18, 6.04, 1.59; 9-335)
15 *Schairerite* 174 (2.99, 2.69, 1.74; 2-0668)
16 *Stercorite* 230
1 *Sulfohalite* 174 (d 3.56, 2.91, 1.76; 3-0345)
6 *Thomsenolite* 36 (d 4.02, 1.96, 2.00; 5-0343)
1 *Tschermigite* (NH_4-alum) 154 (d 4.33, 4.08, 3.27; 7-22)
17 *Wattevillite* 167
18 Yttrocalcite 37

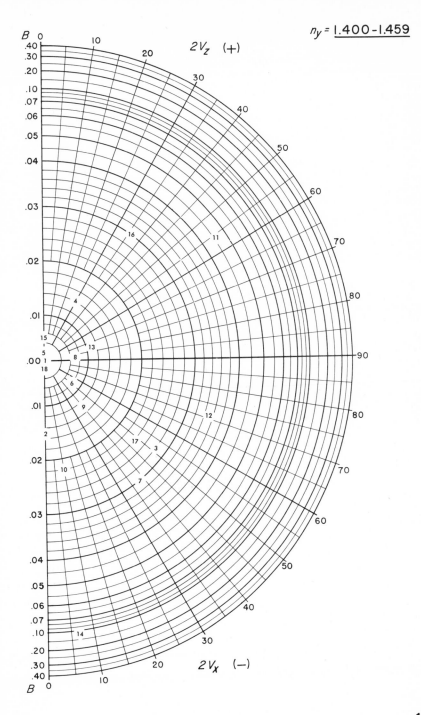

$n_y = \underline{1.400 - 1.459}$

$2V_z \quad (+)$

$2V_x \quad (-)$

19

Isotropic

1 *Paulingite* [Kamb *et al.* AM 45 79–91] (d 8.29, 6.88, 4.78, 3.261, 3.078; auth.)

Anisotropic

2 *Aluminite* 173 (d 9.0, 7.8, 3.72; 8-55)

3 Alunogen 145 (d 4.42, 3.95, 2.48; 1-0348), *boussingaultite* 168

4 Arduinite 336, mordenite 339,(d 3.48, 3.22, 9.10; 6–0239/40), tridymite 249 (d 4.30, 4.08, 3.81; 3–0227*)

5 *Bøggildite* [Pauly 1956, MA 13 206]

6 BORAX 143 (d 2.57, 2.84, 4.86; 1-1097)

3 *Boussingaultite* 168

7 Carnallite 34 (d 3.30, 2.92, 4.65; 8-75)

8 *Chile-loeweite* 166

9 CHRYSOCOLLA 420 (data vary widely) (d 4.35, 1.38, 3.36; 3-0219)

10 Creedite 176 (d 3.48, 7.3, 6.9; 8-72)

11 *Erionite* 337 (d 11.43, 4.32, 2.858; Deffeyes, 1959, AM 44 501)

12 *Ettringite* 174 (d 9.73, 5.61, 3.88; 9-414)

13 *Ferrierite* 337 (d 9.61, 3.99, 3.54; Staples 1955, AM 40 1095, 1955)

25 *Gagarinite* [Stepanov *et al.* 1961, AM 47 805] (d 1.709, 1.726, 2.085, 1.129d; auth.)

14 Gmelinite 335 (d 4.10, 12.0, 2.96; 9-419)

15 Kernite 143 (d 3.12, 7.4, 6.63; 4-0595)

16 *Lansfordite* 121

17 *Lapparentite* 164

18 *Laubanite* 348

19 Melanterite 159 (d 4.90, 3.78, 3.23; 1-0255)

4 Mordenite 339 (d 3.48, 3.22, 9.10; 6–0239/40)

20 NATROLITE 340 (d 2.86, 5.90, 4.38; 3–0705)

21 *Paraluminite* 176

1 *Paulingite* [Kamb *et al.* AM 45 79–91] (d 8.29, 6.88, 4.78, 3.261, 3.078; auth.)

22 *Picromerite* 167

23 Thenardite 169 (d 2.78, 4.66, 3.18; 5-0631)

24 Tincalconite 143 (d 2.94, 4.42, 2.21; 8-49)

4 Tridymite 249 (d 4.30, 4.08, 3.81; 3-0227*)

25 *Gagarinite* [Stepanov *et al.* 1961, AM 47 805] (d 1.709, 1.726, 2.085, 1.129d; auth.)

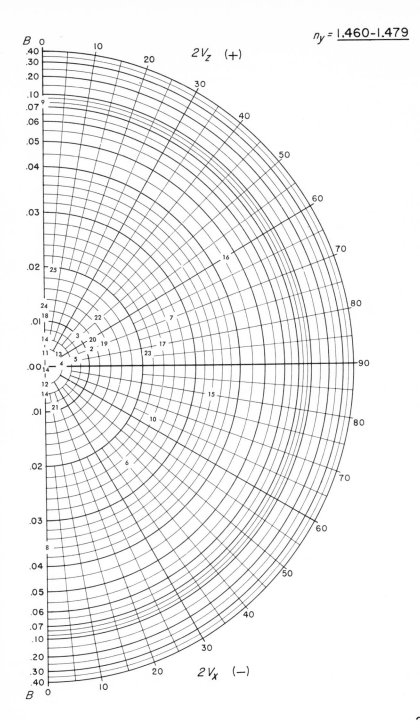

$n_y = \underline{1.460-1.479}$

21

1.480–1.499

Isotropic
  1 Allophane 531 (d 11.0, 3.30, 2.20; 2-0039)
  1 ANALCIME 333 (d 3.43, 5.61, 2.93; 7-340)
  1 *D'Ansite* [Autenrieth *et al.* 1958, AM 43
      1221]
  1 *Evansite* 235
  1 Faujasite 333 (d 15.0, 3.75, 5.68; 2-0010)
  1 Noselite 350 (d 3.69, 2.61, 2.13; 2-0339)
  1 SODALITE 348 (d 3.63, 2.08, 6.3; 3-0338)
  1 SYLVITE 25 (d 3.15, 2.22, 1.82; 4-0587)

Anisotropic and isotropic
  1 Allophane 531 (d 11.0, 3.30, 2.20; 2-0039)
  2 *Ammonioborite* 140
  1 ANALCIME 333 (d 3.43, 5.61, 2.93; 7-340)
  3 *Aphthitalite* 169 (d 2.81, 2.02, 2.92;
      6-0461*), Beryllosodalite [Semenov 1960
      and Sørensen 1960, AM 46 241] (d 3.95,
      2.53, 2.05, 6.15, 2.37; auth.)
  4 *Apjohnite* 146
  5 *Arcanite* 169 (d 2.90, 3.00, 2.89; 5-0613)
  6 *Bayleyite* [Axelrod *et al.* 1951, AM 36 1]
      (d 13.1, 7.66, 3.83; Axelrod *et al.*)
  7 "*Bechilite*" 142
  3 *Beryllosodalite* [Semenow 1960; Sørensen
      1960; AM 46 241] (d 3.95, 2.05, 6.15,
      2.37; auth.)
  8 *Bianchite* 159 (d 4.40, 4.05, 2.92; 1-0352)
  9 Bloedite 167 (3.25, 4.53, 2.71; 4-0549),
      vanthoffite 166
  10 Burkeite 179 (d 2.78, 3.78, 2.58; 2-0840)
  11 *Calclacite* [Van Tassel 1945, MA 10 101]
  12 CHABAZITE 334 (d 2.95, 4.35, 9.5;
      10-370)
  13 Cristobalite 250 (d 4.04, 2.49, 2.85;
      4-0379)
  14 *Dachiardite* 348, *yugawaralite* [Sakurai *et
      al.* 1952, MA 12 133, AM 38 426] (d 5.69,
      4.71, 3.72; auth.)
  1 *D'Ansite* [Autenrieth *et al.* 1958, AM 43
      1221]

15 *Darapskite* 180
16 *Dietrichite* 146
17 *Douglasite* 33
  1 *Evansite* 235
  1 Faujasite 333 (d 15.0, 3.75, 5.68; 2-0010)
18 *Fluellite* 31 (d 6.60, 3.29, 2.66; 2-0121)
19 Goslarite 155 (d 4.21, 5.36, 4.18; 9-395)
20 Halotrichite 146, *phosphorrösslerite* 215,
      STILBITE 345 (d 4.08, 9.1, 4.68; 10-43
21 Hanksite 178,(d 3.78, 2.78, 2.61; 4-0414),
      loeweite 166
22 HEULANDITE 347 (d 3.98, 9.80, 8.50;
      2-0292)
23 *Kalicinite* 125 (d 2.84, 3.68, 2.62; 1-0976)
24 *Leonite* 167, PHILLIPSITE 343 (d 7.64,
      6.91, 3.18; 2-0084)
25 Levynite 335
21 *Loeweite* 166
26 *Magnesium chalcanthite* 160
27 *Misenite* 170 (d 3.85, 3.40, 3.01; 1-0477)
28 *Moraesite* [Lindberg *et al.* 1953, AM 38
      1126; MA 12 301] (d 7.00, 3.278, 4.24;
      auth.)
29 *Morenosite* 155 (d 4.20, 5.30, 2.85; 1-0403
  1 Noselite 350 (d 3.69, 2.61, 2.13; 2-0339)
30 *Paraffin* 132
24 PHILLIPSITE 343 (d 7.64, 6.91, 3.18;
      2-0084)
20 *Phosphorrösslerite* 215
31 *Pickeringite* 146
  1 SODALITE 348 (d 3.63, 2.08, 6.3; 3-0338
20 STILBITE 345 (d 4.08, 9.1, 4.68; 10-433)
32 *Struvite* 214 (d 4.28, 2.93, 2.69; 5-0316
      — ?)
  1 SYLVITE 25 (d 3.15, 2.22, 1.82; 4-0587)
33 *Tamarugite* 160
34 Trona 126 (d 3.06, 2.66, 9.42; 2-0601)
  9 *Vanthoffite* 166
14 *Yugawaralite* [Sakurai *et al.* 1952; MA 12
      133, AM 38 426] (d 5.69, 4.71, 3.72;
      auth.)

22

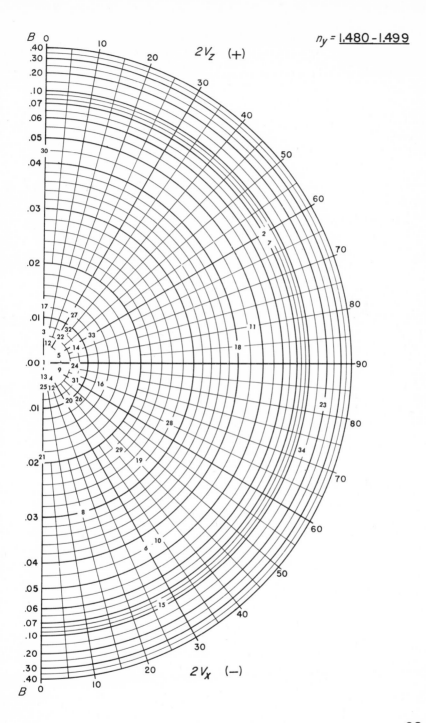

$n_y = \underline{1.480 - 1.499}$

23

1.500–1.519

Isotropic

1 *Cadwaladerite* 32
1 *Dixeyite* [Marmo 1959, AM 45 255] (d 3.32, 3.40, 3.09, 2.27; auth.)
1 Haüynite 350 (d 3.72, 2.63, 6.45; 2-0331)
1 LAZURITE 350 (d 10.0, 3.74, 2.99; 2-0052)
1 LEUCITE 251 (d 5.33, 3.42, 3.24; 6-0124)
1 Mesolite 341 (B = .0005) (d 2.85, 3.19, 6.61; 3-0711)
1 *Northupite* 126 (d 2.69, 2.48, 8.00; 2-0916)
1 *Planerite* 211
1 Pollucite 253 (d 3.44, 2.94, 3.68; 9-461)
1 *Tacharanite* (tobermorite gp.) [Sweet et al. 1961, MM 32 745–753] (d 12.7, 3.05, 2.89, 2.79, 1.82; auth.)
1 Tychite 177

Anisotropic and isotropic

3 *Bischofite* 30 (d 4.10, 2.65, 2.88; 1-0431)
4 *Brewsterite* 347 (d 6.40, 4.60, 3.24; 2-0124)
1 *Cadwaladerite* 32
5 Cancrinite 354 (d 3.19, 4.61, 3.61; 3-0503), hydrotalcite 75)
6 *Carnegieite* 255 (d 4.29, 2.61, 1.50; 2-0259 —high temp. form)
7 *Didymolite* 455
1 *Dixeyite* [Marmo 1959, AM 45 255] (d 3.32, 3.40, 3.09, 2.27; auth.)
8 Epistilbite 346
9 *Evenkite* [Skropyshev 1953, MA 12 305]
10 *Ezcurrite* [Muessig et al. 1957, MA 13 623] (d 6.94, 3.08, 2.77; auth.)
11 *Felsöbányite* 175 (d 3.1, 4.58, 4.24; 8-68)
12 *Flagstaffite* 133
13 Gaylussite 123 (d 10.6, 2.67, 2.58; 9-482*)
14 *Gonnardite* 337 (d 2.92, 5.93, 4.44; 10-473)
15 HARMOTOME 344 (d 8.24, 7.17, 6.26; 9-480)
1 Haüynite 350 (d 3.72, 2.63, 7.45; 2-0331)
5 Hydrotalcite 75
16 *Inderborite* 142
17 *Inderite* 142 (d 5.00, 7.31, 3.18; 8-160*)
18 *Inyoite* 141 (d 3.03, 7.59, 2.29; 6-0361)
19 *Kainite* 173
20 *Karpinskyite* [Shilin 1956, MA 13 209]
21 *Kladnoite* 132
22 *Kurnakovite* 142
23 *Larderellite* 139
24 LAUMONTITE 342 (d 10.0, 9.00, 4.07; 2-0047)
24 *Wegscheiderite* [Fahey et al. 1961, AM 47 415] (d 2.957, 2.646, 2.214, 2.831; auth.)
1 LAZURITE 350 (d 10.0, 3.74, 2.99; 2-0052)
25 *Leifite* 355

24

26 *Letovicite* 170
1 LEUCITE 251 (d 5.33, 3.42, 3.24; 6-0124*
54 *Loughlinite* [Fahey et al. 1960, AM 45 270] (d 12.8, 4.45, 3.79, 3.65, 2.90, 4.80; auth.)
1 Mesolite 341 (d 2.85, 3.19, 6.61; 3-0711)
27 Montmorillonite 398 (d 11.9, 4.45, 2.56; 2-0037*)
28 *Mountainite* [Gard et al. 1957, AM 43 624] (d 2.94, 6.6, 13.1; auth.)
29 Nahcolite 125 (d 2.94, 2.61, 2.21; 3-0653 —
30 *Nesquehonite* 120 (d 6.50, 3.86, 2.61; 1-0130)
31 *Newberyite* 214 (d 3.45, 3.05, 5.90; 1-059
32 Niter 129 (d 3.78, 3.73, 3.03; 5-0377)
33 *Nitromagnesite* 129 (d 4.42, 2.93, 3.29; 1-03
34 *Nocerite* 38, retgersite 154 (d 4.25, 4.57, 2.96; 8-470)
1 *Northupite* 126 (d 2.69, 2.48, 8.00; 2-0916
35 Petalite 260 (d 3.73, 3.65, 3.50; 9-475*) strontioborite [Lobanova 1960, MA 15 363] (d 7.33, 4.09, 3.50, 3.32, 3.06, 2.03.
36 *Pirssonite* 123 (d 2.50, 5.10, 2.65; 2-1051
1 *Planerite* 211
1 Pollucite 253 (d 3.44, 2.94, 3.68; 9-461)
37 *Prosopite* 37 (d 4.35, 2.13, 1.84; 5-0307)
38 *Rabbittite* [Thompson et al. 1955, AM 40 201; MA 12 566] (d 8.24, 7179, 4.37; 7-365/6)
39 *Racewinite* 422
34 *Retgersite* 154 (d 4.25, 4.57, 2.96; 8-470)
40 *Rhodesite* [Gard et al. 1957, AM 43 624] (d 3.07, 3.02, 2.78)
41 Scolecite 341
42 *Stepanovite* [Nefedov via Mokievsky 1953. Mem. Soc. Russe Min. (2) 82 317; MA 123£
35 *Strontioborite* [Lobanova 1960 MA 15 363] (d 7.33, 4.09, 3.50, 3.32, 3.06, 2.033; auth.)
43 *Swartzite* [Axelrod et al. 1951, AM 36 1; MA 11 309] (d 8.76, 5.50, 7.31)
44 *Syngenite* 166
45 Taylorite 170 (d 2.92, 4.21, 3.04; 8-71)
46 Teepleite 135
47 THAUMASITE 179 (d 9.67, 5.50, 3.76; 2-0061)
1 Tychite 177
48 Ulexite 140 (d 12.3, 4.15, 7.8; 9-483*)
49 *Ungemachite* 173
50 *Uranospathite* 206
51 *Uranothallite* 103 (d 5.37, 6.81, 3.16; 6-01
52 *Ussingite* 443 (d 2.95, 2169, 6.35; 2-0710
24 *Wegscheiderite* [Fahey et al. 1961, AM 47 415] (d 2.957, 2.646, 2.214, 2.831; auth
53 *Wellsite* 344
54 *Loughlinite* [Fahey et al. AM 45 270] (d 12.8, 4.45, 3.79, 3.65, 2.90, 4.80; auth

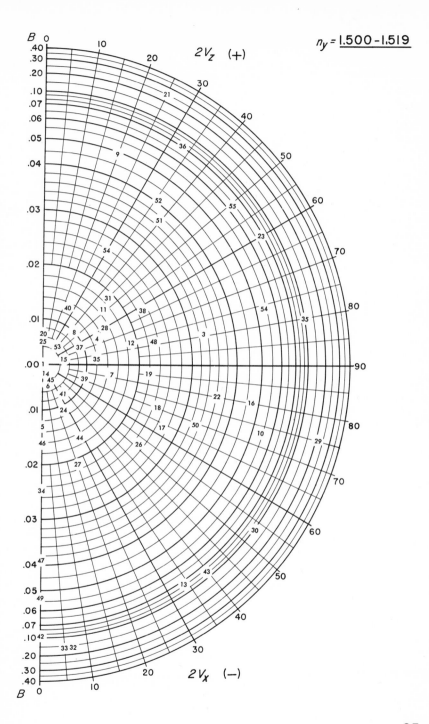

$n_y = 1.500 - 1.519$

$2V_z$ (+)

$2V_x$ (−)

B

25

Isotropic
1 *Aidyrlite* 531
1 Halloysite 400 (hydrated, d 4.42, 10.1, 3.34; 9-451)
1 *Kehoeite* 235
1 *Langbeinite* 165 (d 3.14, 2.67, 4.06; 3-0532)
1 Pollucite 253 (d 3.44, 2.94, 3.68; 9-461)
1 *Spadaite* 422

Anisotropic and isotropic
1 *Aidyrlite* 531
2 ALBITE 276 (high-temperature form, d 3.18, 3.75, 3.21; 10-393*)
3 *Andersonite* [Axelrod *et al.* 1951, AM 36 1; MA 11 309] (d 13.0, 7.97, 5.68; 4-0080), weddellite 131
4 ANORTHOCLASE 276 (d 3.21, 3.24, 4.11; 9-478*)
5 *Artinite* 127 (d 2.74, 5.34, 3.69; 6-0484)
6 Ashcroftine 334
7 *Baeumlerite* 34
8 "*Bechilite*" 142, *fluoborite* 136, *zincaluminite* 174
9 *Berlinite* 183 (d 3.37, 4.28, 1.84; 10-423)
10 *Bikitaite* [Hurlbut 1957, AM 42 792; MA 13 661] (d 4.19, 3.48, 3.40)
11 *Bobierrite* 194 (d 6.70, 2.94, 2.69; 1-0122)
12 *Botryogen* 164, *ginorite* 140 (d 7.18, 5.36, 2.09; 8-116)
13 *Bradleyite* 232 (d 3.32, 2.66, 2.57; 3-0438)
14 *Brugnatellite* 75
15 Chalcanthite 160 (d 4.70, 5.45, 3.97; 8-89)
16 Chalcoalumite 176 (d 8.92, 8.29, 4.24; 8-142)
17 *Chalconatrite* [Frondel 1955, MA 13 6]
18 Copiapite 147, *earlandite* 131
18 *Earlandite* 131
19 *Fairchildite* 123 (d 3.23, 6.40, 3.03; 10-390*)
20 *Fibroferrite* 163
8 *Fluoborite* 136
12 *Ginorite* (= *cryptomorphite*) 140 (d 7.18, 5.36, 2.09; 8-116)
21 Glauberite 165 (d 3.13, 6.22, 2.66; 2-0556)
22 GYPSUM 157 (d 7.56, 3.06, 4.27; 6-0046/7)
1 Halloysite 400 (hydrated, d 4.42, 10.1, 3.34; 9-451)
23 Hyalophane 276, MICROCLINE 276 (d 3.24, 4.21, 3.83; 10-479)
24 *Hydroboracite* 141, *lardere llite* 139
25 *Hydromagnesite* 124 (d 5.79, 2.90, 2.15; 8-179)
26 *Ivanovite* [Nefedov *via* Mokievsky 1953, MA 12 352]
27 *Kaliborite* 140

28 Kaliophilite 257 (d 3.10, 2.60, 3.41; 9-471), *milarite* 257
1 *Kehoeite* 235
29 Kieserite 156 (d 3.38, 4.82, 2.55; 1-0638)
30 *Koktaite* 166 (? d 3.04, 3.19, 5.70; 2-0615)
1 *Langbeinite* 165 (d 3.14, 2.67, 4.06; 3-053)
24 *Lardere llite* 139
31 *Manasseite* 75
32 Mascagnite 169 (d 4.27, 3.08, 3.00; 8-77*)
33 *Mellite* 131
34 *Meyerhofferite* 142 (d 8.39, 6.51, 3.17; 6-003)
23 MICROCLINE 276 (d 3.24, 4.21, 3.83; 10-47)
28 *Milarite* 257
35 *Minasragrite* 92
36 *Minyulite* 208 (d 5.6, 3.37, 6.8; 2-0143)
37 *Nekoite* [Gard *et al.* 1956, MA 14 60]
54 *Nobleite* [Erd *et al.* 1961 AM 46 560] (d 6.79, 3.39, 5.18,4.68, 3.45; auth.)
38 ORTHOCLASE 276 (d 3.18, 4.02, 3.80; 9-46
1 Pollucite 253
39 *Probertite* 139 (d 3.44, 2.94, 3.68; 9-461)
40 *Quetenite* 164
41 Saponite 399 (d 18.8, 1.54, 2.61; 6-0002)
42 *Searlesite* 421 (d 8.01, 4.06, 3.48; 6-0037)
43 Sepiolite 444 (d 7.16, 4.80, 3.55; 7-48)
44 *Sideronatrite* 168
45 *Siderotil* 160
46 *Slavikite* 162
1 *Spadaite* 422
55 Strontioginorite [Braitsch 1959, AM 45 478] (d 7.25, 2.10, 5.40, 3.92, 3.34, 1.19; auth.)
1 *Tacharanite* (tobermorite gp.) [Sweet *et al.* 1961, MM 32 745-753] (d 12.7, 3.05, 2.89, 2.79, 1.82; auth.)
47 *Tachyhydrite* 36
48 *Tavistockite* 229
49 *Teschemacherite* 125 (d 3.00, 5.34, 3.62; 9-415)
50 Thomsonite 336 (d 2.86, 2.95, 2.68; 9-490)
55 *Tunellite* [Erd *et al.* 1961, AM 47 416] (d 6.57, 4.525, 3.867, 5.138, 3.592, 2.503; auth.)
51 *Volkovite* [Nefedov *via* Mokievsky 1953, MA 12 352]
52 *Wapplerite* 215
53 Wavellite 209 (d 8.39, 3.44, 3.20; 2-0075)
3 *Weddellite* 131 (d 2.78, 6.23, 2.24; 4-0702)
8 *Zincaluminite* 174
54 *Nobleite* [Erd *et al.* 1961, AM 46 560] (d 6.79, 3.39, 5.18, 4.68, 3.45; auth.)
55 *Tunellite* [Erd *et al.* 1961 AM 47 416] (d 6.57, 4.525, 3.867, 5.138, 3.592; auth.), *Strontioginorite* [Braitsch 1959, AM 45 478] (d 7.25, 2.10, 5.40, 3.92, 3.34, 1.19; auth.)

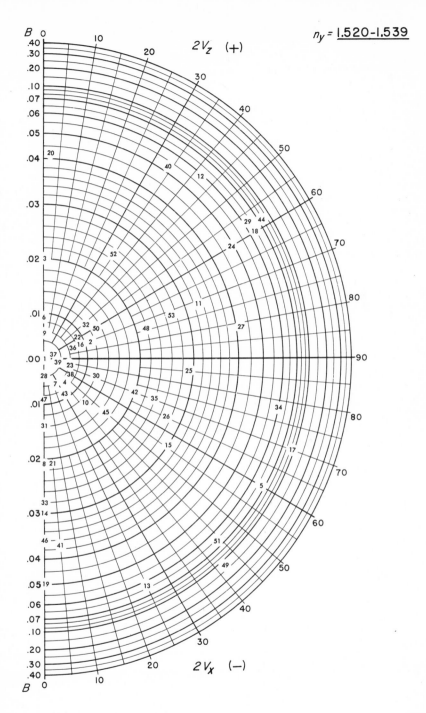

B 0
.40
.30
.20
.10
.07
.06
.05
.04
.03
.02
.01
.00
.01
.02
.03
.04
.05
.06
.07
.10
.20
.30
.40
B 0

$2V_z$ (+)

$n_y = \underline{1.520\text{-}1.539}$

$2V_x$ (−)

27

1.540–1.559

Isotropic
1 APOPHYLLITE 395 (d 3.94, 2.98, 1.58; 7-170)
1 HALITE 24 (d 2.82, 1.99, 1.63; 5-0628)
1 Metahalloysite 400 (d 4.42, 7.5, 3.63; 9-453)
1 *Neotocite* 422
1 *Succinite* 133

Anisotropic and isotropic
2 *Alumohydrocalcite* 124
3 ANDESINE 276 (d 3.21, 3.18, 4.04; 10-359), *miloschite* 363, OLIGOCLASE 276 (d 3.18, 4.03, 3.20; 9-457)
1 APOPHYLLITE 395 (d 3.94, 2.98, 1.58; 7-170)
4 *Armenite* 340
5 *Barbertonite* 76
6 *Bassanite* 158 [Allen *et al.* 1953, AM 38 1266] (d 2.98, 2.78, 5.98; 2-0675)
7 *Beryllite* [Kuzmenko 1954, MA 12 569], LEPIDOLITE (paucilithionite) 371 (d 2.58, 1.99, 10.0; 10-491*; polytypic)
8 Beryllonite 213 (d 2.84, 3.65, 2.28; 6-0443)
9 Botryogen 164
10 *Brushite* 215 (d 2.60, 4.20, 3.02; 4-0740)
11 *Chkalovite* 401
12 CHRYSOTILE 379
13 *Cobalt chalcanthite* 160
14 *Coquimbite* 145 (d 8.26, 2.76, 5.45; 6-0040)
15 CORDIERITE 470 (d 8.58, 3.38, 3.04; 9-472*)
16 *Dawsonite* 126
17 Edingtonite 338
18 *Epididymite* 444
19 Eucryptite 257
20 *Eudidymite* 445
21 *Ferrinatrite* 166
58 *Farringtonite* [Dufresne *et al.* 1961, MA 15 212] (d 3.83, 3.41, 2.39; auth.)
22 *Foshallassite* 478
23 Gismondine 339 (d 7.30, 3.24, 2.73; 2-0096)
24 *Gordonite* 211
25 *Grothine* 479
26 *Gunnbjarnite* [Bøggild 1951, MA 11 517]
27 Gyrolite 395 (d 22, 3.12, 11.0; 9-449)
1 HALITE 24 (d 2.82, 1.99, 1.63; 5-0628)
28 *Hydrocalumite* 101
29 *Julienite* 131 (d 3.55, 3.23, 1.38; 2-0372)
7 LEPIDOLITE (paucilithionite) 371 (d 2.58, 1.99, 10.0; 10-491*; polytypic)

30 LEPIDOLITE (polylithionite) 371 (d 2.58, 1.99, 10.0; 10-491*; polytypic)
31 *Lithiophosphate* [Matias *et al.* 1957, MA 13 383]
32 *Louderbackite* 147
33 *Lueneburgite* 227
1 Metahalloysite 400 (d 4.42, 7.5, 3.63; 9-453)
34 *Metavariscite* 187 (d 2.72, 1.96, 2.22; 2-0894)
3 *Miloschite* 363
35 *Minguzzite* [Garavelli 1955, MA 13 86; AM 41 370] (d 6.9, 3.61, 2.18; 1-0108)
36 Montmorillonite 398 (d 14, 4.41, 2.51; 3-0016*)
37 *Mooreite* 176 (d 10.4, 5.14, 8.29; 5-0094)
38 *Morinite* 227
1 *Neotocite* 422 (d 3.00, 4.18, 3.27; 9-458*)
39 NEPHELINE 254, SCAPOLITE (marialite) 352 (d 3.44, 3.03, 3.78; 2-0412*)
3 OLIGOCLASE 276 (d 3.18, 4.03, 3.20; 9-457)
40 *Osumilite* [Miyashiro 1953, MA 12 304] (d 3.24, 7.17, 5.08; 10-413)
41 Oxammite 131 (d 2.67, 6.32, 3.06; 7-757)
42 *Paravauxite* 211
43 *Pholidolite* 396
44 QUARTZ 246 (d 3.34, 4.26, 1.82; 5-0490)
45 *Rhomboclase* 155
46 SCAPOLITE (dipyre) 352
39 SCAPOLITE (marialite) 352 (d 3.44, 3.03, 3.78; 2-0412*)
56 Schoderite [Hansen 1962, AM 47 637–648] (d 7.9, 15.8, 11.1, 3.06, 9.6; auth.)
47 *Schroeckingerite* 180 (d 7.2, 4.81, 2.88; 6-0054)
48 *Shortite* 123 (d 2.57, 6.03, 5.37; 8-109)
49 *Stichtite* 75
50 *Studtite* 104
1 *Succinite* 133
51 *Sulfoborite* 179
52 *Taeniolite* 373
53 *Vauxite* 211
54 *Veatchite* 139 (d 10.3, 3.33, 2.60; 7-314)
55 Vermiculite 396 (d 14.2, 3.52, 1.53; 10-418)
56 *Voglite* 104, Schoderite [Hansen 1962, AM 47 637–648] (d 7.9, 15.8, 11.1, 3.06, 9.6; auth.)
57 *Whewellite* 132 (d 5.95, 3.65, 2.36; 6-0106)
58 *Zincsilite* [Smol'yaninova *et al.* 1960, MA 15 365] (d 15.3, 1.528, 2.56; auth.), *Farringtonite* [Dufresne *et al.* 1961, MA 15 212] (d 3.83, 3.41, 2.39; auth.)

28

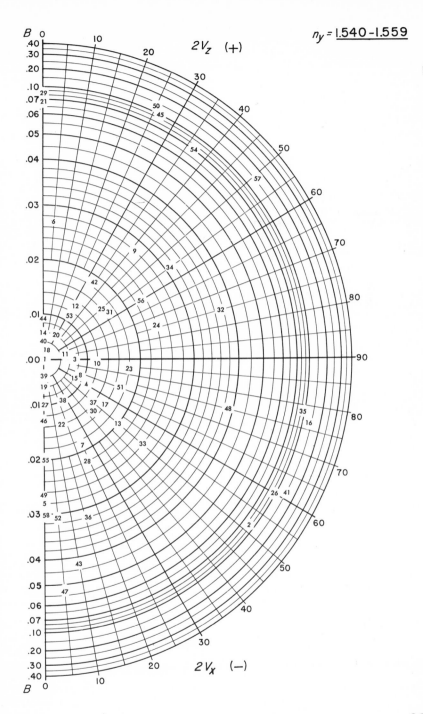

$n_y = \underline{1.540 - 1.559}$

$2V_z$ (+)

$2V_x$ (−)

29

1.560–1.579

Isotropic
1 Gutsevichite [Ankinovich 1959, AM 46
   1200] (d 4.082, 2.506, 1.820, 1.446,
   3.510; auth.)
1 Manganolangbeinite 165
1 Ranquilite [de Abeledo et al. 1960, AM 45
   1078–1086](d 9.26, 4.47, 3. 03, 8.12; auth.)

Anisotropic and isotropic
2 Alunite 170 (d 1.90, 1.75, 3.00; 4–0865)
3 Anauxite 400, haiweeite [McBurney 1959,
   AM 44 839] (d 4.60, 4.08, 7.40; 2–0204)
4 Anhydrite 149 (d 3.50, 2.85, 2.33; 6–0226)
5 "Asbophite" 380
6 Augelite 221 (d 3.53, 3.36, 4.72; 8–69),
   isoclasite 227
7 Autunite 205 (d 10.3, 4.96, 3.59; 8–314*)
8 Banalsite 260 (d 3.50, 3.19, 2.07; 5–0421)
9 Bassetite 206 (d 4.89, 3.46, 8.59; 7–228)
10 Bavenite 259 (d 3.33, 4.14, 3.70; 6–0267),
   tobermorite [new data: McConnell 1954,
   Min. Mag. 30 293] (d 11.3, 2.83, 5.55;
   10–373*)
11 BIOTITE (eastonite) 373 (d 10.1, 3.37,
   2.66; 2–0045)
12 BIOTITE (phlogopite) 373 (d 10.1, 3.37,
   2.66; 2–0045)
13 Brucite 73 (d 2.37, 4.77, 1.79; 7–239)
14 BYTOWNITE 276 (d 3.20, 4.03, 3.75;
   9–467)
15 Calcioferrite 210, lawrencite 29 (d 2.54,
   5.9, 1.80; 1–1106), zeophyllite 359
   (d 12.3, 3.04, 2.91; 8–187)
16 CHLORITE (antigorite) 384 (d 2.51, 7.28,
   3.60; 10–402*) ishkyldite 380, kaolinite
   362 (d 7.15, 3.57, 2.33; 5–0143*), nacrite
   363 (d 3.58, 7.17, 4.41; 7–350*)
17 Cookeite 378 (d 2.32, 3.53, 1.49; 10–397)
18 Dickite 363 (d 7.15, 3.58, 2.33; 10–446*)
19 Elpidite 454, frolovite [Petrova 1957, MA
   14 60]
20 Englishite 226 (d 9.3, 2.86, 1.72; 2–0063)
21 Errite 396, portlandite 75 (d 2.63, 4.90,
   1.93; 4–0733)
22 Fichtelite 133
19 Frolovite [Petrova 1957, MA 14 60]
23 Gibbsite 77 (d 4.85, 4.37, 2.39; 7–324)
24 Görgeyite [Mayrhofer 1953, MA 12 132]
1 Gutsevichite [Ankinovich 1959, AM 46
   1200] (d 4.082, 2.506, 1.820, 1.446,
   3.510; auth.)
3 Haiweeite [McBurney 1959, AM 44 839]
   (d 9.14, 4.556, 4.42; *)
25 Hannayite 215

26 Hoernesite 193 (d 7.01, 8.19, 3.02; 8–141,
   manganoan)
27 Humboldtite 131
16 Ishkyldite 380
6 Isoclasite 227
16 Kaolinite 362 (d 7.15, 3.57, 2.33; 5–0143/4*
29 Kroehnkite 167
30 LABRADORITE 276 (d 3.20, 3.18, 4.04;
   9–465*), Nifontovite [Malinko et al.
   1961, AM 47 172] (d 2.41, 7.04, 2.21,
   3.79, 3.66, 3.02; auth.)
15 Lawrencite 29 (d 2.54, 5.9, 1.80; 1–1106)
31 Lembergite 363
32 Lovozerite 454
1 Manganolangbeinite 165
33 Metasideronatrite 168
34 Metavauxite 211 (d 2.75, 4.67, 4.32; 2–085
35 Mikheevite [Nefedov via Mokievsky 1953,
   MA 12 352]
36 Montgomeryite 210
37 Montmorillonite 398 (d 15.3, 4.50, 3.07;
   3–0009*)
16 Nacrite 363 (d 3.58, 7.17, 4.41; 7–350*)
38 Natroalunite 171, pinnoite 138
30 Nifontovite [Malinko et al. 1961, AM 47
   172] (d 2.41, 7.04, 2.21, 3.79, 3.66,
   3.02; auth.)
39 Norbergite 513 (d 1.74, 3.08, 2.26; 2–1345)
40 Overite 209
38 Pinnoite 138 (d 2.90, 3.17, 3.39; 10–355)
41 Polyhalite 162, variscite 186 (d 5.31,
   4.26, 3.05; 8–157)
21 Portlandite 75 (d 2.63, 4.90, 1.93; 4–0733)
42 Pyroaurite 75, vermiculite 396 (d 14.2,
   3.52, 1.53; 10–418)
43 Quenstedtite 146
44 Reedmergnerite [Milton et al. 1955, MA 12 5
1 Ranquilite (aggreg., fine-grained) [de Abel
   edo et al. 1960, AM 45 1078–1086]
   (d 9.26, 4.47, 3.3, 8.12; auth.)
45 Roemerite 147 (d 4.75, 4.06, 5.02; 4–0267)
46 Saléeite 205 (d 9.85, 3.49, 4.95; 8–313*)
47 Saponite (griffithite) 399 (d 18.8, 1.54,
   2.61; 6–0002)
48 Shilkinite 420
49 Sjögrenite 75
50 Spherite 230
51 Stilpnomelane 390(d 11.9, 4.04, 3.03; 2–0036
52 Tengerite 103
10 Tobermorite [new data: McConnell 1954,
   Min. Mag. 30 293] (d 3.07, 1.83, 11;
   6–0359*)
53 Trudellite 174
41 Variscite 186 (d 5.31, 4.26, 3.05; 8–157*)
42 Vermiculite 396 (d 14.2, 3.52, 1.53; 10–418*
54 Wagnerite 219
15 Zeophyllite 359 (d 12.3, 3.04, 2.91; 8–187)

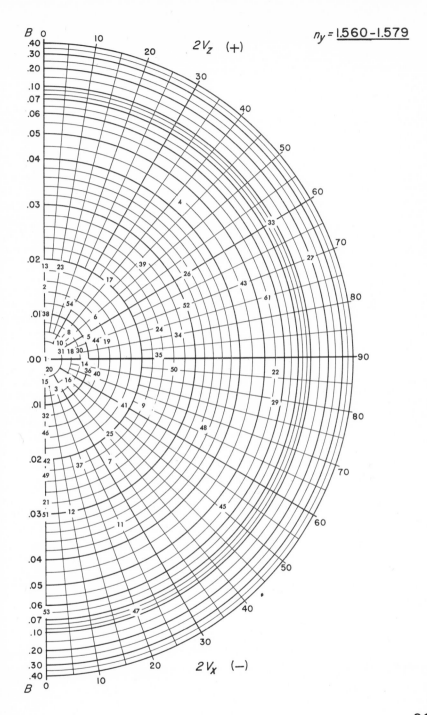

$n_y = \underline{1.560 - 1.579}$

$2V_z \ (+)$

$2V_x \ (-)$

1.580-1.599

Isotropic

1 *Chinglusuite* [Dorfman 1954, MA 13 209]
1 *Ekanite* [Anderson 1961, AM 46 1516; MA 15 358] (metamict)
1 *Gutsevichite* [Ankinovich 1959, AM 46] (d 4.082, 2.506, 1.820, 1.446, 3.510; auth.)
1 *Hydrocerite* [Vlasov *et al.* 1959, AM 45 1132] (amorphous to X-rays)
1 *Zaratite* 128
1 *Zunyite* 482 (d 1.64, 2.69, 1.53; 3-1127)

Anisotropic and isotropic

2 *Abernathyite* [Thompson 1956, AM 41 82; MA 13 86] (d 9.14, 3.84, 3.34; 8-298), scapolite (mizzonite) 352 (d 3.47, 3.08, 2.07; 2-0405)
3 *Ajoite* [Schaller *et al.* 1958, AM 43 1107] (d 12.4, 6.19, 3.34)
4 *Alumian* 162
5 Amblygonite 223 (d 4.64, 3.15, 2.92; 8-102)
6 ANORTHITE 276 (d 3.21, 3.19, 4.05; 10-379*)
7 *Astrolite* 401
8 BERYL 463 (d 2.87, 3.25, 7.98; 9-430)
9 *Buetschlitte* 123 (d 2.86, 3.03, 2.69; 6-0428)
10 *Bultfonteinite* 518 (d 1.93, 8.12, 2.92; 8-223)
11 Cacoxenite 225
12 *Canbyite* 400
13 *Catapleiite* 454
14 Celsian 276, *Guerinite* [Nefedov 1961, AM 47 416] (d 1.87b, 3.48, 3.88, 3.26b, 2.69, 2.47; auth.)
15 *Ceruleolactite* 208, *wardite* 224
1 *Chinglusuite* [Dorfman 1954, MA 13 209]
16 CHLORITE (+penninite) 384 (d 7.19, 4.80, 3.60; 10-183*) (d 2.55, 2.69, 5.90; 3-0856)
17 *Chlormanganokalite* 33, *combeite* [Sahama *et al.* 1957, MA 14 60] (d 2.657, 2.607, 3.304), rinneite 33
18 Chrysocolla 420 (data vary widely) (d 4.35, 1.48, 3.36; 3-0219)
19 Colemanite 141 (d 3.13, 5.64, 3.85; 6-0331)
17 *Combeite* [Sahama *et al.* 1957, MA 14 60] (d 2.657, 2.607, 3.304)
20 *Connarite* 396
21 *Crandallite* 230 (d 2.94, 2.16, 5.70; 5-0615)
22 Cuspidine 480
23 *Duplexite* 357
1 *Ekanite* [Anderson 1961, AM 46 1516] (metamict)
24 Ganophyllite 391
25 Glauconite (skolite) 377 (d 10.1, 2.59, 4.53; 9-439)
14 *Guerinite* [Nefedov 1961, AM 47 416] (d 1.87b, 3.48, 3.88, 3.26b, 2.69, 2.47; auth.)
1 *Gutsevichite* [Ankinovich 1959, AM 46 1200; MA 15 362] (d 4.082, 2.506, 1.820,

1.446, 3.510; auth.)
26 *Hambergite* 137
27 *Heidornite* [Engelhardt *et al.* 1956, MA 13 3)
28 α-*Hopeite* 190 (d 9.04, 4.57, 2.86; 9-497* α- or β- ?)
29 β-*Hopeite* 190 (see also no. 28) *metazeu- nerite* 207 (d 8.76, 3.71, 3.28; 4-0112*)
30 *Howlite* 139 (d 6.2, 3.10, 3.90; 10-410*)
1 *Hydrocerite* [Vlasov *et al.* 1959, AM 45 1132] (amorphous to X-rays)
31 *Ježekite* 233 (d 2.92, 3.47, 2.64; 5-0609)
32 *Johannite* 101 (d 3.83, 6.16, 3.42; 6-0194
33 *Knipovichite* [Nefedov via Mokievsky 195 MA 12 352]
34 *Lanthanite* 103
35 *Leightonite* 162
36 LEPIDOLITE (zinnwaldite) 371 (d 2.58, 1.99, 10.0; 10-491*; polytypic)
37 Leucophanite 476
38 *Metavoltine* 163
29 *Metazeunerite* 207 (d 8.76, 3.71, 3.28; 4-01)
39 *Millisite* 224
40 MUSCOVITE 367 (d 10, 3.35, 2.56; 7-32* polytypic)
41 MUSCOVITE (picrophengite) 367 (see no.
42 *Nitratite* 129 (d 3.03, 2.31, 1.90; 7-271)
43 Nontronite 398 (d 15.4, 4.56, 1.52; 2-0008
44 *Peligotite* [Melkov 1942, MA 12 461]
45 *Pharmacolite* 214
46 *Priceite* 140 (d 10.9, 3.63, 5.46; 9-147)
47 Pyrophyllite 361 (d 3.07, 4.43, 2.42; 3-057
17 *Rinneite* 33
48 *Sabugalite* [Frondel 1951, AM 36 671; MA 11 412] (d 9.69, 4.86, 3.47; 5-0107*)
49 *Saléeite* 205 [Frondel, 1951, AM 36 680; MA 11 413] (d 9.85, 3.49, 4.95; 8-313*)
2 SCAPOLITE (mizzonite) 352 (d 3.47, 3.08 2.07; 2-0405*)
50 *Scholzite* [Strunz 1950, MA 11 189]
61 *Sigloite* [Hurlbut *et al.* 1962, AM 47 1-8] (d 9.69, 6.46, 4.86, 3.23; auth.)
51 *Sterrettite* 208 (d 4.88, 4.51, 2.90; 2-0177)
52 Stilpnomelane 390
53 *Szmikite* 157 (d 3.51, 3.15, 2.59; 1-0565)
54 TALC 364 (d 2.49, 4.58, 1.53; 3-0881)
55 *Torbernite* 206 (d 10.3, 4.94, 3.58; 8-360)
56 *Torreyite* 176 (d 13.1, 5.35, 3.85; 5-0074)
57 *Uranospinite* 206 (d 8.85, 3.59, 3.34; 8-319*; two hydration states)
58 Variscite 186 (d 5.31, 4.26, 3.05; 8-157*)
59 Vermiculite 396 (d 14.2, 3.52, 1.53; 10-418
15 *Wardite* 224
60 Xonotlite 455 (d 3.09, 3.70, 1.50; 9-310)
1 *Zaratite* 128
1 *Zunyite* 482 (d 1.64, 2.69, 1.53; 3-1127)
61 *Sigloite* [Hurlbut *et al.* 1962, AM 47 1-8] (d 9.69, 6.46, 4.86, 3.23; auth.)

32

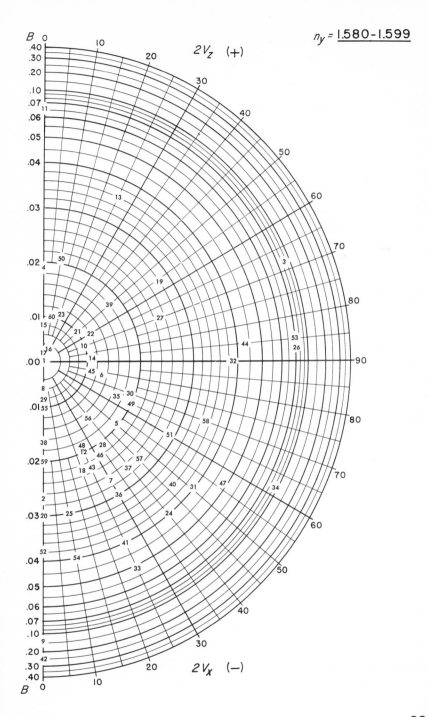

$n_y = \underline{1.580 - 1.599}$

$2V_z$ (+)

$2V_x$ (−)

33

Isotropic
1 *Gutsevichite* [Ankinovich 1959, AM 46
   1200; MA 15 362] (d 4.082, 2.506, 1.820;
   auth.)
1 *Hsianghualite* [Huang *et al.* 1958, MA 15
   362] (d 2.746, 2.209, 2.090, 1.753, 3.443;
   auth.)
1 *Mauritzite* [Tokody 1957, MA 13 381]
1 *Nicolayite* 496
1 *Voltaite* 154

Anisotropic and isotropic
2 *Amarantite* 164
3 Amblygonite 223 (d 4.64, 3.15, 2.92; 8-102)
4 *Anapaite* 195
5 Bertrandite 479
6 *Brazilianite* 221 (d 5.04, 2.98, 2.73;
   6-0136)
7 *Cebollite* 511
8 *Chalcophyllite* 233
9 *Chloraluminite* 31
10 CHLORITE (prochlorite) 381 (d 7.16, 4.80,
   3.55; 7-48*)
11 Chondrodite (yellow) 513
12 *Coesite* [Coes 1953, MA 12 409] (d 3.09,
   3.43, 6.20; 8-18)
13 *Crestmoreite* 421
14 *Dennisonite* 225
15 *Eitelite* [Milton *et al.* 1955, MA 12 511]
16 Eudialyte 454 (d 7.19, 5.74, 2.87; 8-355)
17 Fluocerite 31 (d 3.20, 2.01, 1.33; 3-0501)
18 *Foshagite* 507 (d 2.92, 1.74, 6.8; 9-450*)
19 *Fremontite* 223
20 *Goldichite* [Rosenzweig *et al.* 1955, MA
   12 54]
1 *Gutse vichite* [Ankinovich 1959, AM 46
   1200] (d 4.082, 2.506, 1.820; auth.)
21 *Haidingerite* 214
22 Hemimorphite 482 (d 3.10, 6.60, 3.29;
   5-0555)
23 Herderite 220 (d 3.14, 2.86, 2.20; 6-0338)
24 *Hillebrandite* 506 (d 2.92, 4.76, 3.33; 5-51)
25 *Hurlbutite* [Mrose 1952, AM 37 931; MA 12
   131] (d 3.67, 3.03, 2.78; 6-0213)
1 *Hsianghualite* [Huang *et al.* 1958, MA 15
   362] (d 2.746, 2.209, 2.090, 1.753,
   3.443; auth.)
26 *Hydrophilite* 29 (d 4.49, 3.05, 2.33; 1-0338)
56 *Karnasurtite* [Kuz'menko *et al.* 1959;
   Vlasov *et al.* 1959, AM 45, 1133; Ma 15

361] (d 3.10, 2.88, 3.29, 3.49, 1.723;
   auth.)
27 *Ktenasite* [Kokkoros 1950, MA 11 125]
28 *Kurumsakite* [Ankinovich 1954, MA 13 2
29 *Kyanotrichite* 176
30 *Lehiite* 227
31 LEPIDOLITE (protolithionite) 371 (d 2.
   1.99, 10.0; 10-491*; polytypic)
32 *Manandonite* 395
1 *Mauritzite* [Tokody 1957, MA 13 381]
33 *Meliphanite* 476
34 *Metaheinrichite* [Gross *et al.* 1958, AM 4
   1134]
57 Metaschoderite [Hausen 1962, AM 47 63
   648] (d 7.5, 14.9, 11.1, 3.02, 9.6, 4.92
   auth.)
35 Minnesotaite 365 (d 9.53, 2.52, 4.77;
   6-0025)
36 Monetite 214 (d 3.38, 2.99, 2.76; 4-0513)
37 *Narsarsukite* 358
1 *Nicolayite* 496
38 Nontronite 398 (Fig. 276) (d 15.4, 4.56,
   1.52; 2-0008*)
39 Paragonite 370 (d 1.48, 2.51, 3.18;
   10-420*)
40 Pectolite 460 (d 2.89, 3.08, 1.71; 2-0755
41 *Phosphophyllite* 191
42 *Pseudowavellite* 225
43 Pseudowollastonite 456 (d 3.20, 2.79,
   1.96; 10-486)
44 *Sanbornite* 358
45 *Sarcolite* 496 (d 2.75, 3.33, 4.84, 8-186)
46 Sauconite 400 (d 15.4, 2.67, 1.54; 8-445*
   variable hydration)
47 SCAPOLITE (meionite) 352 (d 3.47, 3.08
   2.07; 2-0405*)
48 *Scawtite* 394 (d 3.03, 2.99, 1.89; 10-417*
49 *Spencerite* 227
50 *Stokesite* 454
51 TOPAZ 509 (d 2.96, 1.40, 1.38; 2-0704/
52 TREMOLITE 435 (d 2.69, 3.10, 8.4;
   9-437*)
53 *Tuhualite* 260 (d 7.16, 2.77, 3.18; 10-440
54 Vivianite 192 (d 6.80, 2.97, 2.71; 3-0070
1 *Voltaite*
55 *Weinschenkite* 188
56 *Karnasurtite* [Kuz'menko *et al.* 1959, AM
   45 1133; MA 15 361] (d 3.10, 2.88, 3.2
   3.49, 1.723; auth.)
57 *Metaschoderite* [Hausen, 1962, AM 47 63
   648] (d 7.5, 14.9, 11.1, 3.02, 9.6, 4.92
   auth.)
58 *Wightmanite* [Murdock 1962, AM 47 718-
   722] (d 10.70, 9.07, 3.03, 2.67; auth.)

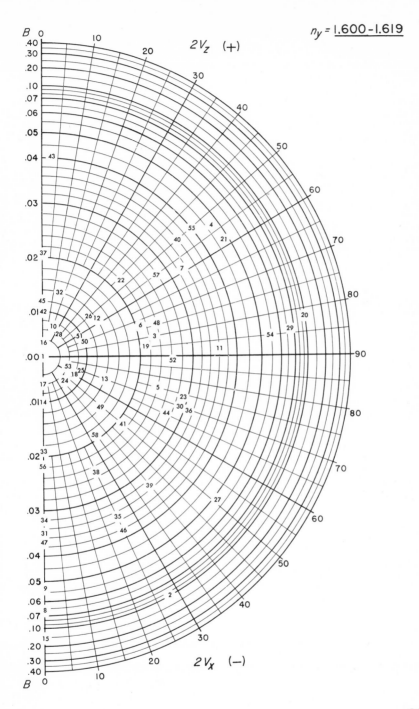

$n_y = \underline{1.600 - 1.619}$

$2V_z \quad (+)$

$2V_x \quad (-)$

Isotropic
1 *Borickite* 233
1 *Pitticite* 180
1 *Spencite* [Frondel 1961, MA 15 460] (meta-mict)

Anisotropic and isotropic
2 *Afwillite* 478 (d 3.19, 2.84, 2.74; 9-454)
3 *Alumoferroasharite* [Serdyuchenko 1956, MA 13 522]
4 ANDALUSITE 521 (d 4.61, 1.49, 5.71; 3-0165*)
5 ANTHOPHYLLITE (Rabbitt no. 30) 425 (d 3.05, 3.24, 8.26; 9-455)
6 ANTHOPHYLLITE (Rabbitt no. 29) 425 (see no. 5) (d 2.82, 3.45, 3.11; 3-0727*)
7 APATITE 197, *dennisonite* 225, *eucolite* 453
8 *Arakawaite* 234, turquois 227 (d 3.68, 2.91, 6.17; 6-0214/5)
9 ARFVEDSONITE 442
10 BARITE 150 (d 3.50, 3.19, 2.07; 5-0421)
11 *Bazzite* 476
12 *Bisbeeite* 420
13 *Bityite* 391
1 *Borickite* 233
14 *Burbankite* [Pecora et al. 1953, AM 38 1169; MA 12 301] (d 2.63, 3.03, 5.26; 6-0513)
15 *Carpholite* 402
16 Celestite 150 (d 2.97, 3.30, 2.73; 5-0593)
17 *Chalcophyllite* 233
18 *Chavesite* [Murdoch 1958, AM 43 1148]
19 CHLORITE (ripidolite) 384 (d 7.07, 14.1, 3.54; 7-76*)
20 Chondrodite (brown) 513
21 *Churchite* 187 (d 4.21, 7.50, 3.02; 8-167)
22 Clinohumite 515
23 *Cymrite* 355 (d 3.95, 2.95, 7.7; 9-476)
24 Danburite 258 (d 3.59, 2.99, 2.73; 2-0362)
7 *Dennisonite* 225
25 *Destinezite* 180
26 *Ephesite* 393
7 Eucolite 453
27 *Faheyite* [Lindberg et al. 1952, AM 38 263; MA 12 131] (d 5.72, 7.28, 3.24; 6-0109/10), woodhouseite 178 (d 2.94, 1.89, 2.19; 4-0670)
28 Garnierite 379 (d 9.8, 1.52, 2.65; 2-0060)
29 *Garrelsite* [Milton et al. 1955, MA 13 86] (d 3.39, 4.41, 3.22; 3-0402)
30 *Gillespite* 357, *mitscherlichite* 33 (d 2.64, 5.4, 2.71; 1-1073)

31 Glauconite 378 (d 10.1, 2.59, 4.53; 9-43*)
32 GLAUCOPHANE 442
33 *Gorceixite* 228, *hamlinite* 228, MELILIT (åkermanite) 473 (d 2.87, 1.76, 3.09; 4-0681*)
34 *Grandidierite* 497
35 *Guildite* 164
33 *Hamlinite* 228
36 *Heinrichite* [Gross et al. 1958, AM 43 1134] (d 3.57, 8.89, 5.03)
37 *Hilgardite* 142
38 Humite 514 (d 1.74, 2.45, 1.48; 7-167/8)
39 *Lausenite* 145
40 Lazulite 203 (d 3.23, 4.72, 3.14; 6-0300)
41 *Mansfieldite* 185 (d 5.45, 4.36, 3.09; 5-0226)
33 MELILITE (åkermanite) 473 (d 2.87, 1.76 3.09; 4-0681*)
42 *Merrillite* 228, *whitlockite* 188 (d 2.88, 2.61, 3.21; 9-169)
43 *Metatorbernite* 207 (d 3.69, 8.66, 3.24; 8-309)
30 *Mitscherlichite* 33 (d 2.64, 5.4, 2.71; 1-1073)
44 *Nordite* 361
45 *Parahopeite* 195 (d 7.56, 2.99, 4.48; 9-49
46 *Parawollastonite* 455 (d 2.97, 3.83, 3.52; 10-489)
47 PARGASITE 435
48 *Picropharmacolite* 191
1 *Pitticite* 180
49 Prehnite 360 (d 3.08, 2.55, 3.48; 7-333)
50 *Sarmientite* 180
51 *Schizolite* 462
52 *Sklodowskite* 530 (d 8.42, 4.19, 3.27; 8-447)
1 *Spencite* [Frondel 1961, MA 15 460] (meta mict)
53 *Suanite* [Watanabe 1953, MA 12 411]
54 *Svanbergite* 178 (d 2.98, 2.22, 5.74; 4-0661)
55 *Szomolnokite* 156 (d 3.42, 4.85, 3.13; 1-0612)
56 *Tilleyite* 480
57 *Troegerite* 207 (d 8.59, 3.79, 3.30; 8-326)
8 Turquois 227 (d 3.68, 2.91, 6.17; 6-0214/5
58 Uranocircite 207
59 α-Uranopilite 100 (d 7.12, 9.18, 4.28; 8-443*)
60 *Wadeite* 453 (d 2.85, 3.85, 5.97; 10-461)
42 *Whitlockite* 188 (d 2.88, 2.70, 2.24; 6-0454)
61 WOLLASTONITE 456 (d 2.97, 3.83, 3.52; 10-487)
27 Woodhouseite 178 (d 2.94, 1.89, 2.19; 4-0670)

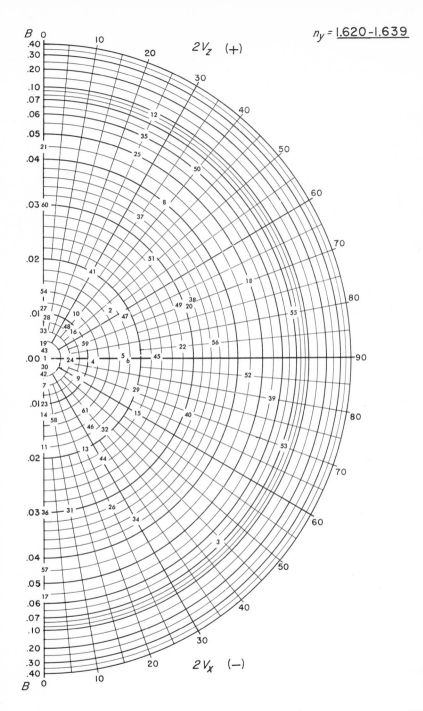

Isotropic
1 *Griphite* 216 (d 2.74, 1.64, 3.07; 7-391)
1 Hisingerite 400 (d 4.44, 2.61, 1.50; 5-0296)
1 *Picite* 195
1 *Salammoniac* 26 (d 2.74, 3.87, 1.58, 7-7)

Anisotropic and isotropic
2 *Aminoffite* 481
3 *Annabergite* 193
4 APATITE 197 (d 2.82, 3.45, 3.11; 3-0727*)
5 *Arrojadite* 189 (d 3.04, 2.72, 3.22; 6-0370)
6 *Auerlite* 496, *goyazite* [Mrose 1952, AM 38 354; MA 12 131] (d 2.97, 2.20, 1.89)
7 *Bementite* 361 (d 2.11, 3.45, 3.11; 3-0982)
8 Boehmite 76 (d 6.11, 3.16, 2.35; 5-0190)
9 *Calciborite* [Petrova 1955, MA 13 208]
10 CALCITE 106 (d 3.04, 2.29, 2.10; 5-0586)
11 *Calkinsite* [Pecora et al. 1953, AM 38 1169; MA 12 301] (d 6.54, 3.27, 4.78)
12 *Callaghanite* [Beck et al. 1953, AM 39 316; MA 12 304]
13 *Childrenite* 226
14 Chondrodite (brown) 513
15 Clinoenstatite 409 (d 2.87, 2.97, 1.60; 3-0696)
16 Clintonite 391
17 *Collinsite* 191
18 DATOLITE 355 (d 3.10, 2.84, 3.75; 3-0557*)
19 Dioptase 453 (d 2.60, 7.28, 2.12; 7-172/3)
20 *Epistolite* 508
21 Euclase 357
22 *Fairfieldite* 191 (d 3.23, 6.40, 3.03; 10-390)
23 *Ferrocarpholite* [de Roever 1951, AM 36 736; MA 11 413]
6 *Goyazite* [Mrose 1952, AM 38 354; MA 12 131] (d 2.97, 2.20, 1.89)
1 *Griphite* 216 (d 2.74, 1.64, 3.07; 7-391)
24 *Guarinite* 518
25 *Hellandite* 518
26 *Herrengrundite* 173
1 *Hisingerite* 400 (d 4.44, 2.61, 1.50; 5-0296)
27 *Hohmannite* 164
28 HORNBLENDE 435 (d 2.70, 3.09, 3.38; 9-434*)
29 *Huréaulite* 215
30 *Inesite* 421
31 JADEITE 416 (d 2.83, 2.42, 2.92; 9-463*), *mosandrite* 517
32 *Jeremejevite* 136 (d 4.27, 1.39, 2.19; 8-183)
33 *Juanite* 420
67 *Kilchoanite* [Agrell et al. 1961, AM 46

1203 and 47 420] (d 2.89, 2.68, 3.07, 3.56, 2.36, 1.964; auth.)
34 *Koninckite* 188
35 *Kotoite* 138 (d 2.67, 2.23, 2.18; 5-0648)
36 *Krausite* 157
37 *Liroconite* 234 (d 6.46, 3.01, 5.95; 4-016
38 *Loseyite* 128
39 *Magniotriplite* [Ginzburg et al. 1951; MA 311] (d 6.46, 3.01, 5.95; 4-0164)
40 Margarite 392
41 Monticellite 502 (d 1.81, 1.59, 2.66; 3-1107/8*)
31 *Mosandrite* 517
42 Mullite 402 (d 3.38, 2.20, 3.41; 6-0258/9
43 *Natrochalcite* 168
44 *Neo-messelite* [Frondel 1955, AM 40 828, MA 13 8] (d 6.34, 3.17, 3.02; 10-389)
45 *Novacekite* [Frondel 1951, AM 36 680; Huang 1956, AM 41 152] (d 10.2, 3.58, 5.06; 8-286)
46 OLIVINE (forsterite) 498 (d 2.46, 2.51, 3.88; 4-0768/9*)
47 *Palermoite* [Mrose 1952, MA 12 131] (d 3.12, 3.66, 2.52; 9-431)
66 *Pargasite, plumbian* [Gillberg 1960, MA 1 291]
48 Phenakite 496, *Sarcolite* 496
1 *Picite* 195
49 *Plumbogummite* 229 (d 2.97, 5.70, 3.45; 2-0683)
50 *Pseudolaueite* [Strunz 1956, MA 13 210]
51 *Rankinite* 477 (d 3.14, 2.69, 3.77; 9-327*)
52 *Ransomite* 145
53 *Reddingite* 190 (d 3.20, 2.74, 4.28; 9-496
54 Rhabdophane 184
55 *Roeblingite* 512
1 *Salammoniac* 26 (d 2.74, 3.87, 1.58; 5-0296)
48 *Sarcolite* 496 (d 2.75, 3.33, 4.84; 8-186)
56 *Serpierite* 155
57 *Shannonite* 504 (d 2.78, 2.18, 2.74; 3-0753*; authenticity??)
58 SILLIMANITE 520 (d 3.36, 2.20, 3.41; 10-369*)
59 *Souzalite* 210 (d 2.69, 3.79, 5.35; 8-165)
60 TOURMALINE (elbaite, dravite) 465
61 *Triplite* 219 (d 3.02, 2.87, 3.19; 5-0583)
62 *Uranochalcite* 101
63 *Veszelyite* 234
64 *Yttroparisite* 122
65 *Zeunerite* 207 (d 3.60, 10.3, 5.07; 8-400*)
66 *Pargasite, plumbian* [Gillberg 1960, MA 1 291]
67 *Kilchoanite* [Agrell et al. 1961, AM 46 1203 and 47 420] (d 2.89, 2.68, 3.07, 3.56, 2.36, 1.964; auth.)

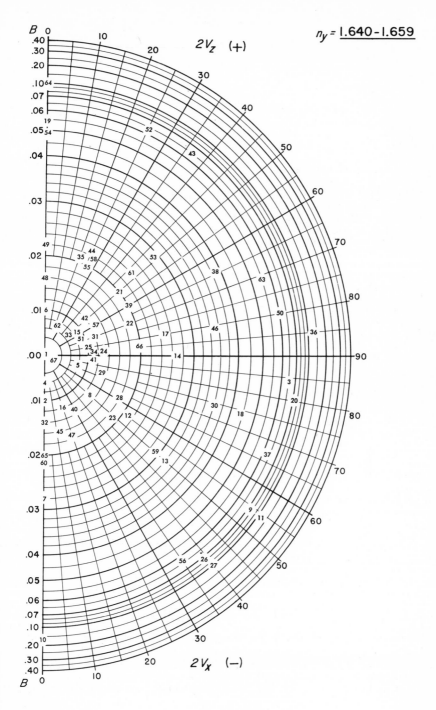

$n_y = 1.640 - 1.659$

39

1.660–1.679

Isotropic
1 *Greenalite* 380
1 *Hibschite* 493 (d 2.68, 3.00, 1.61; 4-0723)
1 *Pharmacosiderite* 204
Anisotropic and isotropic
2 *Acrochordite* 230
3 *Alstonite* 120 (d 3.68, 3.12, 2.13; 3-0322)
STRONTIANITE 118 (d 3.54, 3.45, 2.05; 5-0418)
4 ANDALUSITE 521 (d 4.61, 1.49, 5.71; 3-0165*)
5 ANTHOPHYLLITE (Rabbitt no. 1) 425 (d 3.05, 3.24, 8.26; 9-455)
6 APATITE 197 (d 2.82, 3.45, 3.11; 3-0727*)
7 *Arrojadite* 189 (d 3.04, 2.72, 3.22; 6-0370)
8 *Aurichalcite* 128 (d 3.70, 2.61, 2.71; 9-492)
9 BIOTITE (siderophyllite) 76 (d 10.1, 3.37, 2.66; 2-0045; polytypic)
10 Boracite 139 (d 2.06, 3.04, 2.72; 5-0710*)
11 Bustamite 457 (d 2.89, 1.78, 1.67; 3-0693)
12 *Butlerite* 164
1 *Cahnite* 204
13 *Childrenite* 226
14 CHLORITE (daphnite) 384 (d 13.8, 1.54, 7.00; 2-0028*)
15 *Chloromagnesite* 29 (d 2.56, 1.82, 2.96; 3-0854)
16 *Chlorophoenicite* 229
17 *Clinohedrite* 482
18 Clinohumite 515
19 Cummingtonite 429 (d 2.75, 3.07, 8.38; 7-382)
20 *Cuprosklodowskite* 530 (d 8.18, 4.09, 2.97; 8-290)
21 *Dickinsonite* 214
22 DIOPSIDE 416 (d 2.98, 3.23, 2.94; 9-460*)
23 *Durangite* 221
24 *Ekmannite* 361
25 *Enstatite* (fs = 2%) 406 (d 3.17, 2.87, 2.49; 7-216) *götzenite* [Sahama *et al.* 1957, MA 14 60], *triphylite* 211
26 Erythrite 193 (d 6.69, 3.21, 2.99; 10-480)
27 *Fillowite* 189
28 *Friedelite* 359
29 *Giannettite* 454
30 *Gonyerite* [Frondel 1955, AM 40 1090] (d 7.23, 3.61, 4.79; 10-378)
25 *Götzenite* [Sahama *et al.* 1957, MA 14 60]
1 *Greenalite* 380 (d 2.57, 7.12, 3.56; 2-1012)
1 *Hibschite* 493 (d 2.68, 3.00, 1.61; 4-0723)
31 *Hinsdalite* 178
32 *Johnstrupite* 516, natrophilite 213 (d 2.87, 3.15, 2.61; 5-0620)
33 *Kornerupine* 524 (d 3.01, 2.62, 3.35; 10-457)
34 Lawsonite 482 (d 2.63, 1.55, 2.73; 8-137)
35 Lazulite (Mg : Fe = 1 : 2) 203 (d 3.23, 4.72, 3.14; 6-0300)

36 *Leucosphenite* 455
37 *Lindackerite* 181
38 *Liskeardite* 234
39 *Lotrite* 519
40 *Ludlamite* 226
41 Magnesiodolomite 114 (d 2.88, 1.78, 1.80; 5-0622)
42 *Manganpyrosmalite* [Frondel *et al.* 1953, AM 38 755; MA 12 236]
43 MELILITE (gehlenite; hardystonite) 473 (d 2.85, 1.75, 2.43; 4-0690)
32 Natrophilite 213 (d 2.87, 3.15, 2.61; 5-0620
44 OLIVINE (forsterite) 498 (d 2.46, 2.51, 3.88; 4-0768/9*)
45 *Parabutlerite* 163
46 *Parasymplesite* [Ito *et al.* 1954; MA 12 412] (d 6.83, 7.06, 9.01; 8-189)
47 *Parisite* 122 (d 2.04, 1.28, 2.83; 2-1257), roentgenite [Donnay 1953, AM 38 868; MA 12 238], *synchisite* 122 (d 2.81, 2.05, 1.87; 2-1147)
48 Pennantite 389
1 *Pharmacosiderite* 204
49 *Phosphate-belovite* [Borodin 1954; MA 1246
50 *Pyrosmalite* 359
51 *Reddingite* 190 (d 3.20, 2.74, 4.28; 9-496)
52 *Rinkite* 517
47 *Roentgenite* [Donnay 1953, AM 38 868; MA 12 238]
53 *Roweite* 137
54 *Salmonsite* 190
55 *Sampleite* 225 (d 3.07, 4.35, 1.71; 7-393)
56 *Seamanite* 210, uranophane 529 (d 7.88, 3.94, 2.99; 8-442*)
57 *Sérandite* 443 (d 3.19, 3.00, 2.85; 10-387)
58 *Smirnovite* [Grigoriev *et al.* 1957; MA 14 5
59 *Spodiosite* 222
60 SPODUMENE 419 (d 2.93, 2.80, 1.57; 9-468
61 *Spurrite* 516
62 *Stewartite* 195 (d 9.98, 3.93, 2.99; 5-0110)
63 *Strigovite* 389
3 STRONTIANITE 118 (d 3.54, 3.45, 2.05; 5-0418)
64 *Symplesite* 194 (d 6.79, 7.50, 8.97; 8-172)
47 *Synchisite* 122 (d 2.81, 2.05, 1.87; 2-1147
65 *Szaibelyite* 137
66 Tilasite 221
67 TOURMALINE (schorlite) 465 (d 2.58, 4.00, 4.26; 3-0382*)
25 Triphylite 211
68 *Triplite* 219 (d 3.02, 2.87, 3.19; 5-0583)
56 Uranophane 529 (d 7.88, 3.94, 2.99; 8-442*)
69 *Väyrynenite* [Volborth 1954; MA 12 568] (d 3.45, 2.87, 2.67; 8-139)
70 Witherite 120 (d 3.72, 3.68, 2.15; 5-0378)

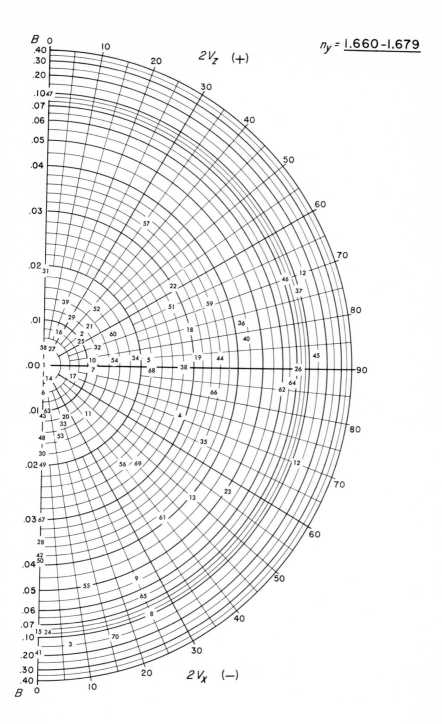

$n_y = \underline{1.660 - 1.679}$

$2V_z \; (+)$

$2V_x \; (-)$

41

1.680–1.699

Isotropic
1 *rhodizite* 135

Anisotropic and isotropic
2 *Antofagastite* 30
3 APATITE 197 (d 2.82, 3.45, 3.11; 3-0727*)
4 ARAGONITE 117 (d 3.40, 1.98, 3.27; 5-0453)
5 *Arsenate-belovite* [Yakhontova *et al.* 1956, AM 42 583; MA 12 352]
6 AUGITE 416 (d 2.99, 1.62, 1.43; 3-0623*)
7 AXINITE 505 (d 2.81, 3.16, 3.46; 6-0448/9)
8 *Bandylite* 138
9 *Barylite* 476
10 *Barytocalcite* 121 (d 3.16, 3.96, 2.54; 1-0770)
42 *Benstonite* [Lippmann 1962, AM 585–598] (d 3.085, 3.92, 2.536, 2.127; auth.)
11 BIOTITE (annite) 373 (d 10.1, 3.37, 2.66; 2-0045; polytypic)
12 *Boltwoodite* [Frondel *et al.* 1956; MA 13 380]
43 *Cenosite* [Heinrich *et al.* 1962, AM 47 328–336] (d 6.50, 2.75, 3.28, 3.19; auth.)
13 *Chlorophoenicite* 229
14 Dumortierite 259 (d 2.55, 5.89, 5.84; 7-71/2)
15 *Erythrosiderite* 34
16 *Euchroite* 226 (d 5.34, 2.83, 7.37; 4-0222)
17 *Florencite* 216 (d 2.93, 5.63, 2.16; 8-143)
18 *Harstigite* 479
19 *Kainosite* 463
20 *Kempite* 32
21 *Koettigite* 193 (d 3.20, 3.00, 2.72; 1-0744*)
22 Kornerupine 524 (d 3.01, 2.62, 3.35; 10-457)

23 *Kupletskite* (= Mn-astrophyllite) [Semenov 1956; MA 13 384]
24 *Legrandite* 210
25 *Nenadkevichite* [Kuzmenko *et al.* 1955, MA 12 569] (d 3.20, 3.10, 1.43; 8-105)
35 *Norsethite* [Mrose *et al.* 1961, AM 46 420–429] (d 3.015, 3.960, 2.656, 2.512, 2.104, 1.931; auth.)
26 OLIVINE (chrysolite) 498 (d 2.77, 2.52, 2.4 7-156*)
27 Oxyhornblende 439
28 PIGEONITE 409
29 Pumpellyite 519 (d 2.90, 3.79, 2.74; 10-447)
1 *Rhodizite* 135
30 Riebeckite 442 (d 8.42, 3.13, 4.51; 9-436*)
31 *Rosenbuschite* 518
32 *Shubnikovite* [Nefedov *via* Mokievsky 1953, MA 12 352]
33 *Sincosite* 204
34 *Spangolite* 175 (d 7.1, 3.59, 2.54; 5-0142)
35 Stilpnomelane 390 (d 11.9, 4.04, 3.03; 2-0036), *Norsethite* [Mrose *et al.* 1961, AM 46 420–429] (d 3.015, 3.960, 2.656, 2.512, 2.104, 1.931; auth.)
36 *Trichalcite* 190
37 Triphylite 211
38 *Triplite* 219 (d 3.02, 2.87, 3.19; 5-0583)
39 β-Uranotile 530
40 Willemite 497 (d 2.63, 2.83, 3.49; 8-492)
41 *Zippeite* 100 (d 7.31, 3.66, 3.15; 8-402)
42 *Benstonite* [Lippmann 1962, AM 47 585–598] (d 3.085, 3.92, 2.536, 2.127; auth.)
43 *Cenosite* [Heinrich *et al.* 1962, AM 47 328–336] (d 6.50, 2.75, 3.28, 3.19; auth.)

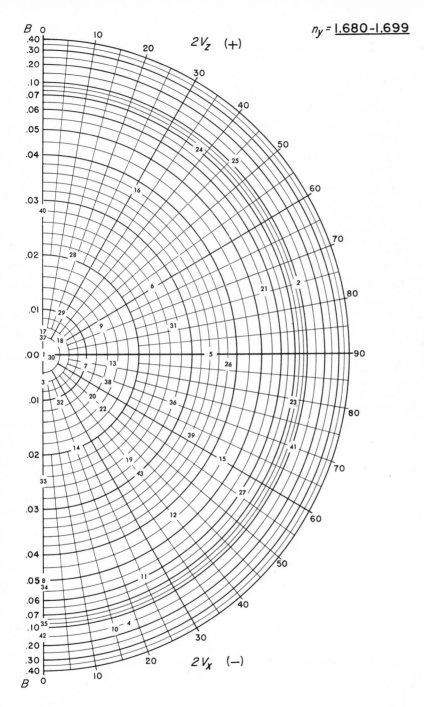

$n_y = \underline{1.680 \text{-} 1.699}$

B 0
.40
.30 $2V_z$ (+)
.20
.10
.07
.06
.05
.04
.03
.02
.01
.00
.01
.02
.03
.04
.05
.06
.07
.10
.20
.30
.40
B 0

$2V_x$ (−)

43

Isotropic
1 *Berzeliite* (Mg type) 188 (d 2.77, 1.65, 1.35; 2-0854)
1 PYROPE 486 (d 2.58, 1.54, 1.07; 2-1008)
1 *Rowlandite* [Frondel 1961, MA 15 460] (metamict)
1 SPINEL 81 (d 2.44, 2.02, 1.43; 5-0672*)

Anisotropic and isotropic
2 *Ancylite* 122
3 APATITE 197 (d 2.82, 3.45, 3.11; 3-0727*)
4 *Astrophyllite* 480
5 *Barylite* 476
6 *Bastnäesite* 121 (d 1.29, 2.86, 2.04; 2-1433)
1 *Berzeliite* (Mg type) 188 (d 2.77, 1.65, 1.35; 2-0854)
7 *Brandtite* 190
8 *Bromellite* 59 (d 2.06, 2.34, 2.19; 4-0843)
9 Clinohumite 515
10 Cummingtonite 428 (d 3.22, 1.87, 1.75; 9-324)
11 EPIDOTE (clinozoisite) 449,(d 2.90, 2.40, 1.64; 9-438), *serendibite* 527
12 *Erikite* 187
13 Ferrohastingsite 435 (d 2.70, 3.09, 3.38; 9-434*; variable)
14 *Ferroschallerite* 359
15 *Gerhardtite* 129 (d 6.85, 3.44, 2.45; 3-0068), *merwinite* 505 (d 2.66, 1.90, 1.53; 4-0728)
16 *Graftonite* 189 (d 2.86, 3.50, 2.72; 6-0423*)
17 *Hidalgoite* [Smith et al. 1953, AM 38 1218; MA 12 302] (d 2.98, 5.73, 3.51; 6-0380), *koivinite* [Frank-Kamenetzky et al. 1953, MA 12 411]
18 HORNBLENDE 435 (d 2.70, 3.09, 3.38; 9-434*)

17 *Koivinite* [Frank-Kamenetzky et al. 1953 MA 12 411]
19 *Labuntzovite* [Semenov et al. 1955, MA 4] (d 3.15, 2.56, 1.54; 9-498*)
20 *Langite* 175
21 *Larnite* 504 (d 2.80, 2.74, 2.78; 9-351)
22 Magnesite 109 (d 2.74, 2.10, 1.70; 8-479)
23 *Magnesium orthite* 452
24 *Magniophilite* [Beus 1950, MA 11 190]
15 *Merwinite* 505 (d 2.66, 1.90, 1.53; 4-0728
25 *Metahohmannite* 164
26 *Neptunite* 463
27 OLIVINE (hyalosiderite) 500 (d 2.79, 2.5 2.48; 7-159*)
28 *Oxychildrenite* [Ginzburg et al. 1950, MA 11 124]
29 *Palmierite* 165
30 Pennaite 454
31 Pumpellyite 519 (d 2.90, 3.79, 2.74; 10-447)
1 PYROPE 486 (d 2.58, 1.54, 1.07; 2-1008
32 *Roselite* 191
1 *Rowlandite* [Frondel 1961, MA 15 460] (metamict)
33 Sapphirine 93
34 *Schallerite* 359
35 *Schoepite* 72 (d 7.49, 3.26, 3.64; 8-396)
11 *Serendibite* 527
1 SPINEL 81 (d 2.44, 2.02, 1.43; 5-0672*)
36 *Strengite* 186 (d 3.30, 3.65, 4.20; 3-0452*
37 *Tarbuttite* 223 (d 6.1, 3.65, 2.76; 8-158)
38 Tinzenite 505 (d 2.81, 3.46, 6.30; 6-0444
39 *Triphylite* 211, zoisite 446
40 *Triplite* 219 (d 3.02, 2.87, 3.19; 5-0583)
41 *Woehlerite* 516 (d 2.84, 3.00, 3.25; 10-46.
42 *Xanthoxenite* 210 (d 3.05, 2.73, 3.22; 5-0571)
39 Zoisite 446

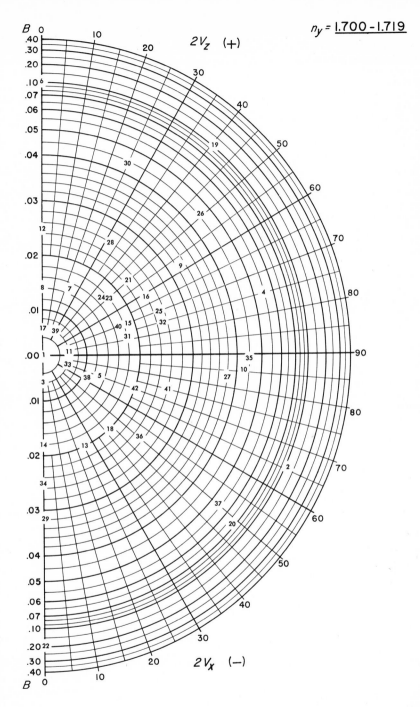

$n_y = \underline{1.700 - 1.719}$

45

1.720–1.739

Isotropic
1 *Delvauxite* 228 (d 4.35, 3.91, 4.06;
4-0329)
1 GROSSULARITE 486 (d 2.65, 1.58, 2.96;
3-0826)
1 *Helvite* 351
1 Periclase 58 (d 2.11, 1.49, 1.22; 4-0829)
1 *Rowlandite* 478

Anisotropic and isotropic
2 *Adamite* 217 (d 2.45, 4.90, 2.97; 6-0536)
3 *Adelite* 218
4 Antlerite 174 (d 4.86, 2.57, 3.60; 7-407/8)
5 Babingtonite 462
48 *Batisite* [Kravchenko *et al.* 1960, AM 45
754 and 1317]
6 *Bermanite* 209
7 *Birnessite* [Jones *et al.* 1956, MA 14 60]
8 Chalcomenite 177
49 *Chambersite* [Honea *et al.* 1962, AM 47
665–671] (d 3.07, 2.74, 2.08, 3.54, 2.17;
auth.)
9 Chloritoid 393 (d 4.44, 2.97, 1.58; 7-398*),
donbassite 512
10 *Cobaltoan roselite* 191
11 *Connellite* 175 (d 8.00, 13.7, 2.29; 8-135)
12 *Curtisite* 133
1 *Delvauxite* 228
13 Diaspore 78 (d 3.99, 2.32, 2.13; 5-0355)
14 *Diderichite* 104
9 *Donbassite* 512
15 Ferrohypersthene 406 (d 3.20, 2.89, 1.49;
2-0520; "hypersthene")
16 *Gageite* 519
17 Glaucochroite 504
1 GROSSULARITE 486 (d 2.65, 1.58, 2.96;
3-0826)
18 HEDENBERGITE 416
1 *Helvite* 351
19 *Hematolite* 231 (d 2.39, 1.56, 6.12;
6-0563)
20 *Homilite* 356
21 Iddingsite 507
50 *Innelite* [Kravchenko *et al.* 1961, AM 47
805] (d 3.92, 3.04, 2.95, 1.964, 1.845,
1.735; auth.)
22 *Johachidolite* 140

23 *Kaersutite* 439
24 KYANITE 527 (d 1.38, 3.20, 1.93; 3-1164)
25 *Landesite* 208
26 *Lopezite* 177
27 *Melanocerite* 509, *stottite* [Strunz *et al.*
1958; AM 43 1006]
28 *Niocalite* [Nickel 1956, AM 41 785; MA 1
211]
29 *β-Roselite* [Frondel 1955, AM 40 828; MA
13 8]
30 Olivine (hyalosiderite) 498 (d 2.79, 2.53,
2.48; 7-157*)
1 Periclase 58 (d 2.11, 1.49, 1.22; 4-0829)
31 *Phosphosiderite* 187
32 *Phosphuranylite* 207 (d 7.91, 3.96, 3.15;
8-289)
33 *Pyrochroite* 74 (d 4.72, 1.37, 2.45; 8-171)
34 *Renardite* 230 (d 7.97, 3.99, 5.93; 8-328)
35 Rhodonite 459 (d 2.94, 2.97, 2.76; 5-0614)
1 *Rowlandite* 478
36 Sapphirine 93
37 *Serendibite* 527
38 *Sicklerite* 189
39 Stilpnomelane 390 (d 11.9, 4.04, 3.03;
2-0036)
27 *Stottite* [Strunz *et al.* 1958, AM 43 1006]
40 *Strengite* 186 (d 4.36, 5.5, 3.12; 2-0250)
41 *Taaffeite* [Anderson *et al.* 1951, MA 11
209] (d 2.43, 2.05, 1.43; 8-11), VESUVI
ANITE 508 (d 2.74, 2.59, 1.63; 2-0867)
42 *Thalenite* 477, *varulite* 213 (d 2.74, 3.50,
2.56; 6-0487)
43 TITANAUGITE 416 (augite: d 2.99, 1.62,
1.43; 3-0623)
44 *Trimerite* 260
45 *Triploidite* 220 (d 2.94, 3.10, 3.19; 5-0611)
46 *Tyrolite* 232
42 *Varulite* 213 (d 2.74, 3.50, 2.56; 6-0487)
41 VESUVIANITE 508 (d 2.74, 2.59, 1.63;
2-0867)
47 Xenotime 183 (d 3.44, 2.56, 1.76; 9-377)
48 *Batisite* [Kravchenko *et al.* 1960, AM 45
754 and 1317]
49 *Chambersite* [Honea *et al.* 1962, AM 47
665–671] (d 3.07, 2.74, 2.08, 3.54, 2.17;
auth.)
50 *Innelite* [Kravchenko *et al.* 1961, AM 47
805] (d 3.92, 3.04, 2.95, 1.964, 1.845,
1.735; auth.)

46

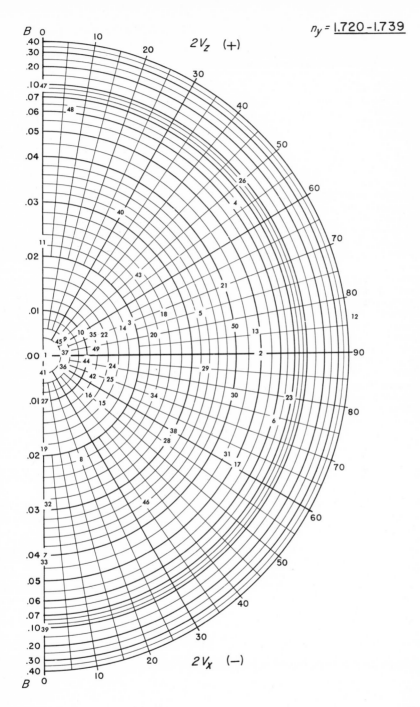

$n_y = \underline{1.720 - 1.739}$

B

$2V_z$ (+)

$2V_x$ (−)

B

1.740–1.759

Isotropic
1 *Arsenolite* 60 (d 3.20, 6.39, 2.54; 4-0566)
1 *Caryocerite* 509
1 *Helvite* (genthelvite) 351
1 *Magnalumoxide* [Bobkov *et al.* 1951, MA 11 365]
1 *Tritomite* 509
1 *Yttrialite* 477

Anisotropic and isotropic
2 *Adamite* 217 (d 2.45, 4.90, 2.97; 6-0536)
3 *Ardennite* 529
1 *Arsenolite* 60 (d 3.20, 6.39, 2.54; 4-0566)
4 *Astrophyllite* 480
5 *Azovskite* 232
6 AZURITE 124 (d 3.50, 5.15, 2.53; 3-0360*), seidozerite [Semenov *et al.* 1958; AM 44 467]
7 *Benitoite* 453
8 *Caracolite* 174
1 *Caryocerite* 509
9 CHRYSOBERYL 89 (d 2.09, 1.62, 3.23; 10-82)
10 *Freirinite* 233
11 *Hagendorfite* [Strunz 1954; MA 12 463]
1 *Helvite* (*genthelvite*) 351
12 *Hodgkinsonite* 515
13 *Hoelite* 133
14 Lamprophyllite 527
15 *Låvenite* 517, olivine (hyalosiderite) 500 (d 2.79, 2.53, 2.48; 7-157*)

16 *Libethenite* 217 (d 4.81, 2.63, 2.91; 1-0274)
17 *Lodochnikovite* [Nefedov *via* Mokievsky 1953, MA 12 352]
18 *Lomonosovite* [Gerasimovsky 1950, MA 11 123]
1 *Magnalumoxide* [Bobkov *et al.* 1951, MA 11 365]
19 Mangandolomite 114
20 *Mixite* 225 (d 11.9, 3.55, 2.46; 8-114)
15 Olivine (hyalosiderite) 500 (d 2.79, 2.53, 2.48; 7-157*)
21 *Planchéite* 421
22 Pyroxmangite 460
23 *Rutherfordite* 122 (d 4.56, 4.25, 3.19; 9-163)
24 *Schafarzikite* 90
25 *Schuilingite* [Guillemin *et al.* 1957, AM 43 796]
26 Scorodite 185 (d 5.56, 4.44, 3.16; 5-0216)
6 *Seidozerite* [Semenov *et al.* 1958, AM 44 467]
27 *Shcherbakovite* [Eskova *et al.* 1954, MA 12 569] (d 2.90, 2.64, 1.69; 8-101)
28 STAUROLITE 522
29 *Sursassite* 452
30 *Tinticite* 234 (2V = "large," sign = ?)
1 *Tritomite* 509
31 *Unnamed* [Frondel 1957, AM 42 743]
32 *Vegasite* 172
33 *Wolfeite* 220 (d 2.93, 3.09, 3.18; 5-0612)
1 *Yttrialite* 477

48

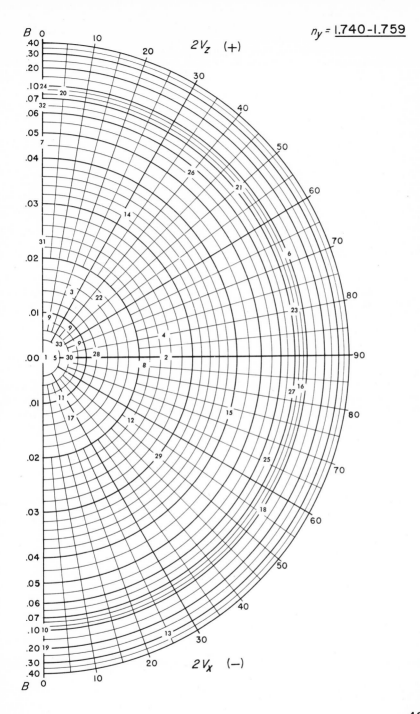

$n_y = \underline{1.740 - 1.759}$

$2V_z$ (+)

$2V_x$ (−)

49

1.760-1.779

Isotropic
1 *Helvite* 351

Anisotropic and isotropic
2 *Adamite* 217 (d 2.45, 4.90, 2.97; 6-0536)
3 *Allactite* 232
4 Allanite 451 (d 2.91, 2.92, 2.86; 10-366*; also metamict)
5 Alluaudite 203 (d 2.71, 6.26, 3.05; 10-419)
6 *Austinite* 219
7 *Belyankinite* [Gerasimovsky et al. 1950, MA 11 123]
8 *Billietite* 72 (d 7.33, 3.77, 3.17; 8-358)
9 Brochantite 175 (d 3.91, 6.5, 2.53; 3-0282)
10 *Calcium-larsenite* 504
11 *Cappelenite* 509
12 Clinoferrosilite 409
13 *Cordylite* 121, ferrodolomite 114
14 CORUNDUM 61 (d 2.09, 2.55, 1.60; 10-173)
15 *Dewindtite* 225
16 EPIDOTE (pistacite) 449 (d 2.90, 2.40, 1.64; 9-438)
17 *Ferrimolybdite* 145
13 Ferrodolomite 114
18 Ferrohypersthene 406 (d 3.20, 2.89, 1.49; 2-0520)

1 *Helvite* (*danalite*) 351
19 *Holdenite* 231 (d 2.99, 3.61, 2.47; 5-0590)
20 *Joaquinite* 463
21 *Leucophenicite* 516 (d 1.81, 2.86, 2.70; 3-1104)
22 *Lombaardite* [Nel et al. 1949, MA 11 127]
23 *Margarosanite* 462
24 *Murmanite* 480
25 *Nordenskiöldite* 136
26 Olivine (hortonolite) 498 (d 2.81, 2.49, 2.55; 7-158)
27 *Orientite* 507
28 *Paradamite* [Switzer 1956, MA 13 380
29 *Paraschoepite* 72
30 *Pseudomalachite* 229 (d 4.48, 2.39, 2.42; 8-163)
31 *Rossite* 228
32 *Sahamalite* [Jaffe et al. 1953, AM 38 741; MA 12 237] (d 3.90, 3.65, 2.87 6-0189)
33 *Simplotite* [Thompson et al. 1956, MA 13 379]
34 *Swedenborgite* 91
35 *Taramellite* 401
36 *β-Uranopilite* 100 (d 7.12, 9.18, 4.28; 8-443*)
37 *Yoshimuraite* [Watanabe et al. 1961, AM 46 1515] (d 3.40, 2.94, 4.90, 3.24, 2.78; auth.)

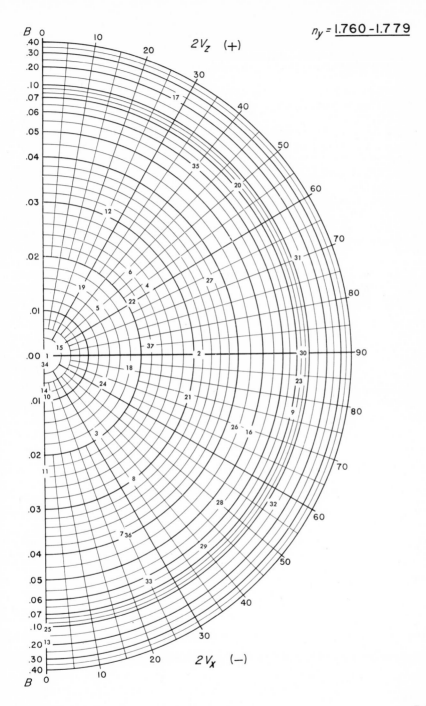

$n_y = \underline{1.760 - 1.779}$

$2V_z$ (+)

$2V_x$ (−)

51

Isotropic
1 *Berzeliite* (*manganoan*) 188 (d 2.77, 1.65, 1.35; 2-0854)

Anisotropic and isotropic
2 ACMITE 416 (d 2.99, 2.54, 6.5; 3-0621*)
3 *Allactite* 232
4 Allanite (mangan-orthite) 452 (d 2.91, 2.92, 2.86; 10-366*; also metamict)
5 *Alleghanyite* 516 (d 1.80, 2.87, 2.65; 2-1332)
6 *Arseniopleite* 216
7 *Barbosalite* [Lindberg *et al.* 1955, AM 40 952; MA 13 85], shattuckite 421
8 *Beraunite* 210
1 *Berzeliite* (manganoan) 188 (d 2.77, 1.65, 1.35; 2-0854)
9 *Caryinite* 189
10 *Cornetite* 231 (d 3.04, 4.29, 3.17; 9-495)
11 Epidote (piedmontite) 449 (d 2.90, 2.40, 1.64; 9-438)
12 *Epiianthinite* 71 (d 7.63, 3.78, 3.20; 8-306)
13 Gadolinite 356 (d 3.10, 2.79, 2.54; 8-190)
14 *Higginsite* 218
15 *Lessingite* 512
16 *Lossenite* 180
17 Monazite 184 (d 3.09, 3.31, 2.88; 4-0612)
18 *Olivenite* 216 (d 2.98, 4.82, 5.91; 4-0657)
19 *Reinerite* [Geier *et al.* 1958, AM 44 207]
20 *Retzianite* 231
21 Scorodite 185 (d 5.56, 4.44, 3.16; 5-0216)
7 *Shattuckite* 421
28 *Stishovite* [Chao *et al.* 1962, AM 47 807] (d 2.959, 1.530, 1.981, 1.235, 2.246, 1.478; auth.)
22 *Stillwellite* [McAndrew *et al.* 1955; MA 13 7]
23 *Taosite* 61
24 *Teineite* 155
25 *Thortveitite* 477
26 *Uraconite* 92
27 *Vandenbrandeite* 101 (d 4.44, 5.26, 2.97; 8-325*)
28 *Stishovite* [Chao *et al.* 1962, AM 47 807] (d 2.959, 1.530, 1.981, 1.235, 2.246, 1.478; auth.)

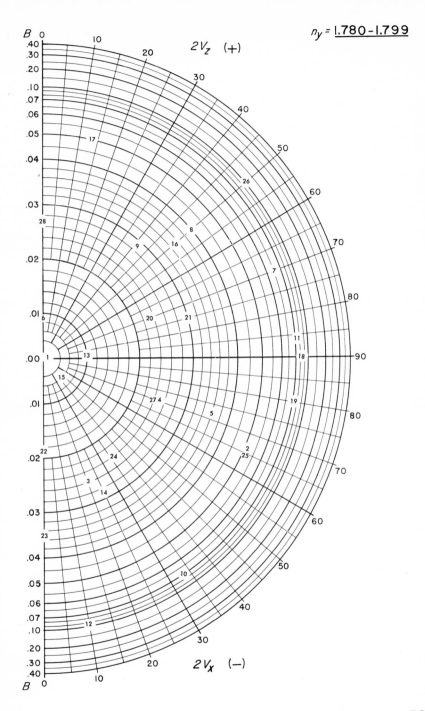

$n_y = \underline{1.780 - 1.799}$

$2V_z$ (+)

$2V_x$ (−)

53

1.800-1.849

Isotropic
1 ALMANDITE 486 (d 2.57, 1.54, 2.87;
9-427)
1 *Beckelite* 520
1 *Bilibinite* [Bur'yanova (1958(?), AM 44
692—a mixture?]
1 Gahnite 81 (d 2.44, 2.86, 1.43; 5-0669)
1 Galaxite 81 (d 2.49, 2.92, 1.46; 10-310)
1 Hercynite 81 (d 2.45, 1.56, 1.43; 7-68*)
1 *Lime* 59 (d 2.41, 1.70, 2.78; 4-0777)
1 *Naegite* 495
1 SPESSARTITE 486 (d 2.60, 1.56, 1.61;
10-354*)

Anisotropic and isotropic
1 ALMANDITE 486 (d 2.57, 1.54, 2.87;
9-427)
2 *Ammoniojarosite* 171
3 *Arsenoclasite* 229
4 *Avelinoite* [Lindberg *et al.* 1954, MA 12
512]
1 *Beckelite* 520
5 *Becquerelite* 72 (d 7.50, 3.22, 3.75; 8-299)
34 *Betpakdalite* [Ermilova *et al.* 1961, AM 47
172] (d 8.75, 3.63, 1.532, 1.480, 2.95;
auth.)
1 *Bilibinite* [Bur'yanova 1958(?), AM 44 692]
6 *Carphosiderite* 172 (d 3.06, 4.9, 1.97;
2-0597), *ferritungstite* 163, jarosite 171
(d 3.08, 3.11, 2.29; 10-443), natrojarosite 171
7 Cerite 507
8 *Chalcosiderite* 227 (d 3.77, 3.39, 3.02;
8-127)
9 *Cornwallite* 230 (d 3.20, 3.52, 2.40; 8-161*)
10 *Cronstedtite* 389
11 *Dietzeite* 130
12 *Dolerophanite* 172
13 Dufrenite 221 (d 3.17, 5.05, 3.42; 8-155)
14 *Enigmatite* 477
6 *Ferritungstite* 163
15 *Flinkite* 231, *leucochalcite* 226
1 Gahnite 81 (d 2.44, 2.86, 1.43; 5-0669)
1 Galaxite 81 (d 2.49, 2.92, 1.46; 10-310)
1 Hercynite 81 (d 2.45, 1.56, 1.43; 7-68*)

16 *Hibonite* [Curien *et al.* 1956, 1957, MA 13
381]
17 *Higginsite* 218
6 *Jarosite* 171 (d 3.08, 3.11, 2.29; 10-443)
18 *Kryzhanovskite* [Ginzburg 1950, MA 11
189–90]
19 *Lautarite* 129 (d 4.27, 3.04, 3.24; 1-0386)
15 Leucochalcite 226
1 *Lime* 59 (d 2.41, 1.70, 2.78; 4-0777)
20 *Linarite* 172 (d 3.12, 3.53, 1.79; 4-0598)
21 *Metatyuyamunite* [Weeks *et al.* via Fleischer 1954, AM 39 1037; MA 12 566–7]
(d 8.51, 4.22, 3.24; 8-310*)
22 *Molybdophyllite* 479
1 *Naegite* 495
6 *Natrojarosite* 171
23 *Nigerite* 89 (d 2.42, 2.85, 1.55; 9-487),
thorite 496 (d 3.56, 1.84, 4.69; 8-318)
24 Olivenite 216 (d 2.98, 4.82, 5.91; 4-0657)
25 Olivine [ferrohortonolite (d 2.82, 2.50,
2.56; 7-163), knebelite, tephroite (d 2.5
3.61, 2.86; 9-485)] 498
26 *Painite* [Claringbull *et al.* 1957, MA 14 61
(d 5.76, 2.52, 3.70; 10-405), *phosphate-
cyrilovite* [Novotny *et al.* 1953, MA 12
512]
27 *Pascoite* 236
26 *Phosphate-cyrilovite* [Novotny *et al.* 1953
MA 12 512]
28 *Pseudomalachite* 229 (d 4.48, 2.39, 2.42;
8-163)
29 Rhodochrosite 109 (d 2.84, 3.66, 1.76;
7-268)
30 *Rockbridgeite* (zincian) [Lindberg *et al.*
1950, AM 35 1028; MA 11 187] (d 3.33,
3.21, 6.99; 6-0270)
31 *Sarkinite* 220
1 SPESSARTITE 486 (d 2.60, 1.56, 1.61;
10-354)
35 *Stranskiite* [Strunz 1960, MA 15 213]
32 *Tagilite* 227
23 Thorite 496 (d 3.56, 1.84, 4.69; 8-318)
33 *Warwickite* 137
34 *Betpakdalite* [Ermilova *et al.* 1961, AM 47
172] (d 8.75, 3.63, 1.532, 1.480, 2.95;
auth.)
35 *Stranskiite* [Strunz 1960, MA 15 213]

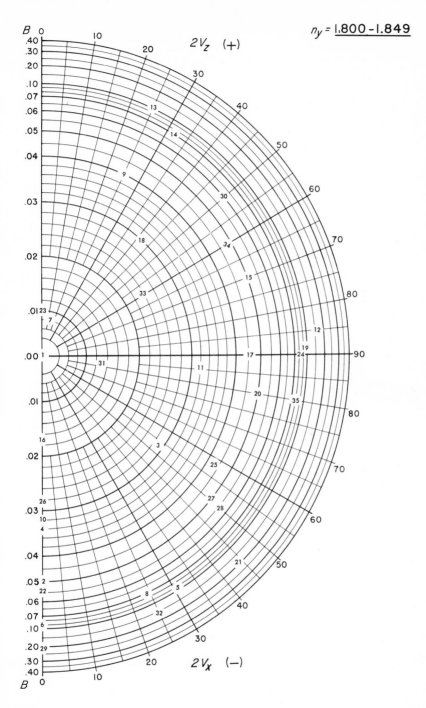

$n_y = \underline{1.800-1.849}$

B 0

$2V_z$ (+)

$2V_x$ (−)

B 0

55

1.850-1.899

Isotropic
1 ANDRADITE 486 (d 2.70, 3.02, 1.61; 10-288)
1 *Bindheimite* 235 (d 3.03, 1.85, 1.58; 7-321)
1 *Chalcolamprite* 90
1 *Ellsworthite* 90
1 *Roméite* 235 (d 2.94, 1.81, 1.55; 7-66)
1 Uvarovite 486 (d 2.65, 1.59, 2.97; 7-70)

Anisotropic and isotropic
1 ANDRADITE 486 (d 2.70, 3.02, 1.61; 10-288)
2 Anglesite 151 (d 3.00, 4.26, 3.33; 5-0577)
3 *Arseniosiderite* 224
4 Atacamite 30 (d 5.40, 5.00, 2.82; 2-0146)
5 *Beaverite* 173
1 *Bindheimite* 235 (d 3.03, 1.85, 1.58; 7-321)
6 *Caledonite* 179
1 *Chalcolamprite* 90
7 *Chevkinite* 443 (d 3.20, 2.74, 4.97; 9-486)
8 Clinoclasite 232 (d 3.56, 3.14, 4.3; 8-154)
9 *Dumontite* 230 (d 4.29, 3.02, 3.75; 8-294)
10 *Dussertite* 225 (d 3.11, 2.32, 2.00; 2-0574)
1 *Ellsworthite* 90
11 Erinite 229 (d 2.46, 4.45, 3.17; 2-1066)
12 *Frondelite* 222 (d 3.20, 3.38, 1.60; 8-83)
27 *Hallimondite* [Walenta *et al.* 1961, AM 47 414]
13 *Hemafibrite* 234
14 *Heterosite* 183
15 *Hoegbomite* 90
28 *Hügelite* [Walenta *et al.* 1961, AM 47 418]
16 Ilvaite 511
17 *Ludwigite* 136
18 MALACHITE 127 (d 2.86, 3.69, 5.06; 10-399)
19 Olivine (fayalite) 498 (d 2.49, 2.82, 3.54; 9-307*)
20 *Plumbojarosite* 172 (d 2.78, 1.72, 3.57; 5-0635)
21 *Rockbridgeite* 222 (d 3.19, 3.39, 1.59; 8-159)
1 *Roméite* 235 (d 2.94, 1.81, 1.55; 7-66)
22 SIDERITE 109 (d 2.79, 1.73, 3.59; 8-133), smithsonite 109 (d 2.75, 3.55, 1.70; 8-449), *spherocobaltite* 111 (d 2.77, 1.71, 3.65; 1-1020)
22 Smithsonite 109 (d 2.75, 3.55, 1.70; 8-449)
22 *Spherocobaltite* 111 (d 2.77, 1.71, 3.65; 1-1020)
23 *Synadelphite* 233
24 *Törnebohmite* 512
25 *Tyuyamunite* 208 (d 10.2, 5.02, 3.20; 6-0017)
26 *Uvanite* 100 (d 2.94, 4.60, 5.79; 8-323*)
1 Uvarovite 486 (d 2.65, 1.59, 2.97; 7-70)
27 *Hallimondite* [Walenta *et al.* 1961, AM 47 414]
28 *Hügelite* [Walenta *et al.* 1961, AM 47 418]

56

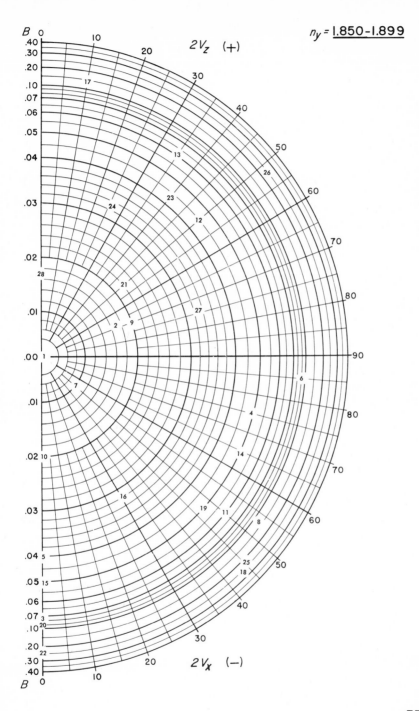

$n_y = \underline{1.850 - 1.899}$

57

1.900-1.949

Isotropic
1 *Betafite* 94 (d 2.98, 1.82, 1.55; 8-300)
1 *Kimseyite* [Milton *et al.* 1961, AM 46 533-549] (d 1.667, 2.539, 2.79; auth.)
(Zr-garnet)

Anisotropic and isotropic
2 *Argentojarosite* 171
3 *Bellingerite* 130
1 *Betafite* 94 (d 2.98, 1.82, 1.55; 8-300)
4 Carnotite 226 (d 6.56, 3.12, 3.53; 8-317)
5 *Claudetite* 65
6 *Corkite* 178
7 *Daubréeite* 32
8 *Duttonite* [Thompson *et al.* 1956, MA 13 378] (d 4.40, 3.61, 1.84; 10-377)
9 *Fersmanite* 527
10 *Fourmarierite* 98 (d 3.09, 3.45, 1.91; 8-295)
11 *Ganomalite* 478
12 *Huttonite* [Pabst 1950, MA 11 188] (d 3.09, 2.89, 4.23; 4-0613)
13 *Ianthinite* 71 (d 7.60, 3.79, 3.59; 8-307*)
14 *Kasolite* 530 (d 3.26, 2.93, 4.18; 8-297)
1 *Kimseyite* [Milton *et al.* 1961, AM 46 533-548] (d 1.667, 2.539, 2.79; auth.)
(Zr-garnet)
15 *Nasonite* 478
16 SCHEELITE 148 (d 3.10, 4.76, 3.07; 7-210*)
17 *Schultenite* 213
18 *Sengierite* 208 (d 9.82, 4.91, 3.74; 8-398)
19 *Trippkeite* 236
20 *Tsumebite* 234
21 *Waltherite* 128 (d 3.11, 3.04, 2.72; 6-0336)
24 *Widenmannite* [Walenta *et al.* 1961, AM 47 415]
22 *Yeatmanite* 529
23 ZIRCON 494 (d 3.30, 4.43, 2.52; 6-0266)
24 *Widenmannite* [Walenta *et al.* 1961, AM 47 415]

58

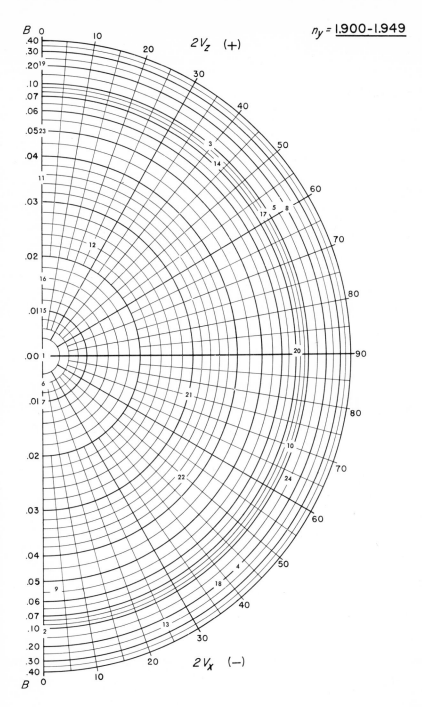

$n_y = \underline{1.900\text{-}1.949}$

59

1.950-1.999

Isotropic
   1 Brannerite [Whittle 1954, MA 13 88] (d 3.42, 1.90, 2.46; 8-2)
   1 *Djalmaite* 94
   1 *Hatchettolite* 90
   1 *Kimzeyite* [Milton *et al.* 1958, AM 43 1006] (garnet group)
   1 *Magnussonite* [Gabrielson 1957, MA 13 381] (d 2.85, 3.12, 2.47; 10-407)
   1 *Nantokite* 26 (d 3.13, 1.92, 1.63; 6-0344)
   1 *Neotantalite* 90
   1 *Samirésite* 94 (d 3.20, 2.50, 4.05; 8-327)

Anisotropic and isotropic
   2 *Alamosite* 455 (d 3.58, 3.36, 5.82; 3-0344)
   3 *Bayldonite* 227 (d 3.14, 3.21, 2.93; 6-0335)
   4 *Beudantite* 178
   1 Brannerite [Whittle 1954, MA 13 88] (d 3.42, 1.90, 2.46; 8-2)
   5 *Calomel* 27 (d 3.16, 4.14, 1.96; 4-0581)
   6 *Carpathite* [Piotrovsky 1955, MA 13 208]
   7 *Chapmanite* 508
   8 *Chevkinite* 443 (d 3.20, 2.74, 4.97; 9-486)
   9 Diaboléite 35 (d 5.51, 3.31, 2.29; 5-0220)
  10 *Dixenite* 236
   1 *Djalmaite* 94
  11 *Francevillite* [Branche *et al.* 1957, MA 13 522]
   1 *Hatchettolite* 90
  12 *Hyalotekite* 401
  13 *Hydrotungstite* 73 (d 3.46, 2.30, 3.30; 6-0244)
   1 *Kimzeyite* [Milton *et al.* 1958, AM 43 1006]
  14 *Larsenite* 504
   1 *Magnussonite* [Gabrielson 1957, MA 13 381] (d 2.85, 3.12, 2.47; 10-407)
  15 *Manganostibite* 92
  16 *Melanovanadite* 100
   1 *Nantokite* 26 (d 3.13, 1.92, 1.63; 6-0344)
   1 *Neotantalite* 90
  17 *Powellite* 148 (d 3.09, 1.93, 1.59; 8-144*)
   1 *Samirésite* 94 (d 3.20, 2.50, 4.05; 8-327)
  18 SPHENE 525 (d 3.20, 2.59, 2.98; 2-0521)
  19 *Uranospherite* 98 (d 3.16, 1.83, 3.87; 8-321)

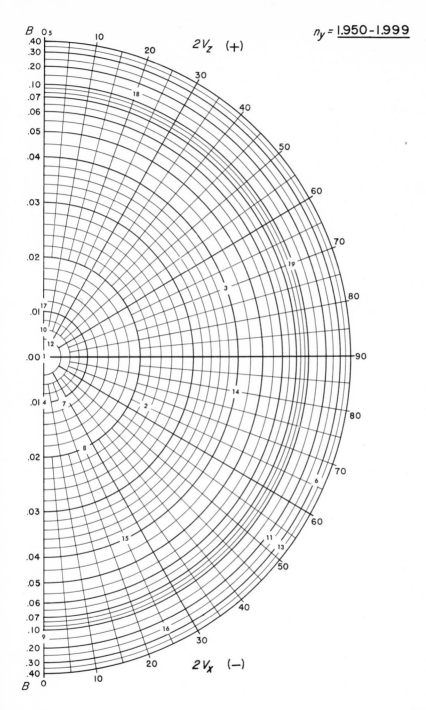

$n_y = \underline{1.950 - 1.999}$

$2V_Z \;\; (+)$

$2V_X \;\; (-)$

61

Isotropic
1 *Picrochromite* 81 (d 2.51, 4.81, 2.08; 10-351)
1 *Wiikite* 97

Anisotropic and isotropic
27 *Baotite* [PengCh'i-Jui 1959, MA 15 135] (d 1.337, 3.55, 2.88, 2.24; auth.)
2 *Barysilite* 476
26 *Calzirtite* [Zdorik *et al.* 1961, AM 46 1515] (d 2.945, 1.801, 1.537, 1.170, 2.552; auth.)
3 CASSITERITE 68 (d 3.35, 2.64, 1.77; 5-0467)
4 *Cervantite* 71
5 *Cumengéite* 37
6 *Fiedlerite* 31
25 *Freudenbergite* [Frenzel 1961, AM 46 765] (d 3.627, 1.911, 5.81, 3.101, 3.105, 2.731, 2.712; auth.)
7 *Gamagarite* 189
8 *Lanarkite* 172
9 *Leadhillite* 179
10 *Lindgrenite* 168 (d 3.50, 4.15, 2.67; 10-395)
11 *Navajoite* [Weeks *et al.* 1954, MA 12 408] (d 12.1, 10.6, 2.90; 7-332)
12 *Perrierite* [Bonatti *et al.* 1950, MA 11 310]
1 *Picrochromite* 81 (d 2.51, 4.81, 2.08; 10-351)
13 *Pseudoboléite* 38
14 *Ramsayite* 401
15 *Simpsonite* 95 (d 1.64, 1.39, 2.84; 3-1128)
16 "*Sodium-hewettite*" [Weeks *et al. via* Fleischer 1954; MA 12 567, AM 39 1038]
17 Sulfur 22 (d 3.85, 3.21, 3.44; 8-247/8)
18 *Turanite* 229
19 *Uzbekite* 191
20 *Volborthite* 218
21 *Voltzite* 43
22 *Walpurgite* 233 (d 3.11, 3.25, 3.05; 8-324)
23 *Wherryite* 179 (d 3.05, 4.57, 3.14; 6-0348)
1 *Wiikite* 97
24 Zinkite 59 (d 2.48, 2.82, 2.60; 5-0664)
25 *Freudenbergite* [Frenzel 1961, AM 46 765] (d 3.627, 1.911, 5.81, 3.101, 3.015, 2.731, 2.712; auth.)
26 *Calzirtite* [Zdorik *et al.* 1961, AM 46 1515] (d 2.945, 1.801, 1.537, 1.170, 2.552; auth.)
27 *Baotite* [Peng Ch'i-Jui 1959, MA 15 135] (d 1.337, 3.55, 2.88, 2.24; auth.)

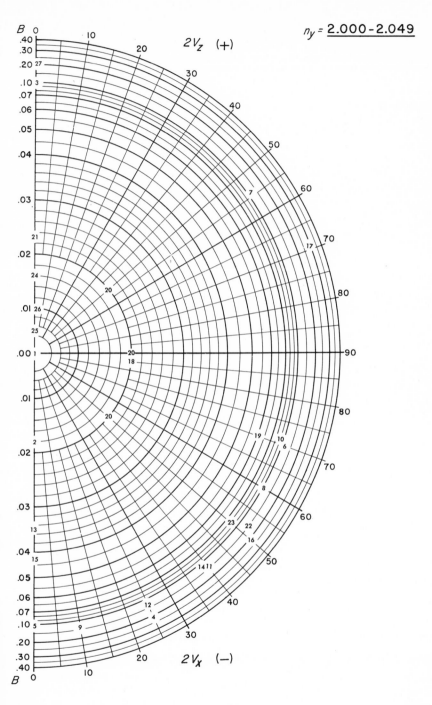

$n_y = \underline{2.000 - 2.049}$

$2V_z$ (+)

$2V_x$ (−)

63

Isotropic
1 Cerargyrite 26 (d 2.77, 1.96, 3.20; 6-0480)
1 *Eulytite* 494 (d 3.26, 2.75, 2.10; 2-0488)
1 Microlite 90 (d 1.57, 1.84, 3.00; 3-1139)
1 *Percylite* 37
1 *Senarmontite* 60 (d 3.22, 1.97, 2.79; 5-0534)

Anisotropic and isotropic
2 *Boléite* 37 (d 4.40, 3.83, 3.13; 2-0240)
3 *Carminite* 203 (d 2.52, 5.80, 3.24; 2-1039)
1 Cerargyrite 26 (d 2.77, 1.96, 3.20; 6-0480)
4 CERUSSITE 119 (d 3.59, 3.50, 2.49; 5-0417)
5 *Clarkeite* 102 (d 3.17, 3.34, 5.77; 8-315)
6 *Duftite* 218 (d 3.17, 2.63, 2.91; 6-0322*)
7 *Emmonsite* 177 (d 3.13, 2.86, 2.51; 7-404)
1 *Eulytite* 494 (d 3.26, 2.75, 2.10; 2-0488)
8 *Hydrocerussite* 123 (d 2.63, 3.60, 3.28; 10-401*)
9 *Hydrohausmannite* [Frondel 1953, AM 38 761; MA 12 237]
1 Microlite 90 (d 1.57, 1.84, 3.00; 3-1139)
10 *Montanite* 172
1 *Percylite* 37
11 *Pinakiolite* 137 (d 2.52, 1.52, 3.02; 10-396)
12 Pyromorphite 200 (d 2.95, 4.09, 2.05; 8-103*)
13 *Salesite* 129
1 *Senarmontite* 60 (d 3.22, 1.97, 2.79; 5-0534)
14 *Vesigniéite* [Guillemin 1955, MA 13 6]

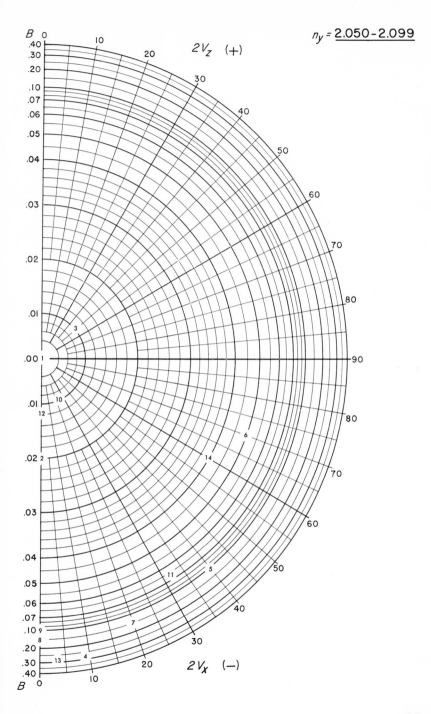

$n_y = \underline{2.050 - 2.099}$

$2V_z$ (+)

$2V_x$ (−)

65

Isotropic

1 *Ampangabéite* 98
1 *Blomstrandinite* 97
1 Chromite 81 (d 2.51, 1.91, 1.61; 4-0759*)
1 Fergusonite 94 (d 3.12, 2.96, 1.90; 9-443*)
1 *Irinite* [Borodin *et al.* 1954, MA 12 462]
1 *Oldhamite* 41 (d 2.85, 2.01, 1.64; 8-464)
1 *Roméite* 235 (d 2.94, 1.81, 1.55; 7-66; for variety "lewisite")
1 *Yttrocrasite* 97
1 *Zirconolite* [Borodin *et al.* 1956, MA 13 383]

Anisotropic and isotropic

1 *Ampangabéite* 98
2 *Beyerite* 128 (d 2.84, 2.14, 1.75; 4-0693), *matlockite* 29 (d 3.56, 3.61, 2.90; 4-0460/1)
1 *Blomstrandinite* 97
1 Chromite 81 (d 2.51, 1.91, 1.61; 4-0759*)
3 *Curite* 98 (d 6.28, 3.97, 3.14; 8-292)
1 Fergusonite 94 (d 3.12, 2.96, 1.90; 9-443)
1 *Irinite* [Borodin *et al.* 1954, MA 12 462]
4 *Laurionite* 30
2 *Matlockite* 29 (d 3.56, 3.61, 2.90; 4-0460/1)
5 *Metahewettite* 236
6 Mimetite 202 (d 3.05, 2.99, 2.10; 2-0609)
1 *Oldhamite* 41 (d 2.85, 2.01, 1.64; 8-464)
7 *Penfieldite* 29
8 *Phosgenite* 126 (d 2.82, 2.23, 3.64; 9-494)
1 *Roméite* 235 (d 2.94, 1.81, 1.55; 7-66; for "lewisite")
9 *Trigonite* 237
1 *Yttrocrasite* 97
1 *Zirconolite* [Borodin *et al.* 1956, MA 13 383]

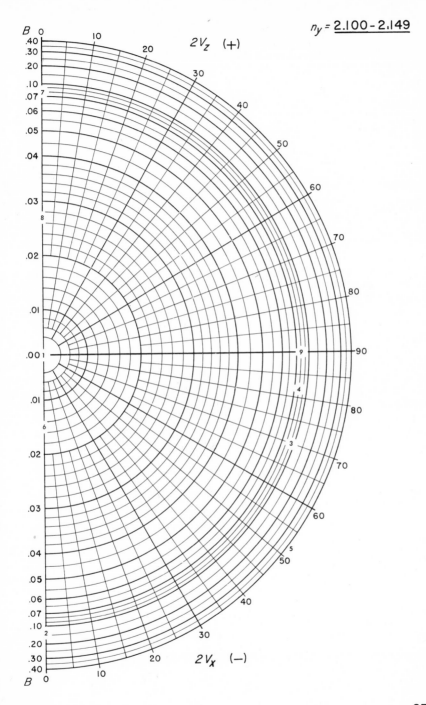

$n_y = \underline{2.100 - 2.149}$

$2V_z \quad (+)$

$2V_x \quad (-)$

67

Isotropic
1 *Blakeite* 177 (d 3.00, 2.54, 1.72; 7-377)
1 Euxenite 97 (d 2.99, 3.66, 2.95; 9-442*)
1 *Koppite* 90 (d 3.00, 1.83, 1.56; 2-0674)
1 *Manganosite* 59 (d 2.22, 2.57, 1.57; 7-230)
1 *Pyrrhite* 90
1 Samarskite 97 (d 2.98, 2.92, 3.13; 10-398*)
1 *Yttrotantalite* 99
1 *Zirkelite* 90

Anisotropic and isotropic
2 *Atelestite* 232 (d 3.23, 3.12, 2.72; 7-388)
3 Baddeleyite 71 (d 3.16, 2.84, 2.62; 7-343)
4 *Bismoclite* 31 (d 3.44, 2.68, 2.75; 6-0249)
1 *Blakeite* 177 (d 3.00, 2.54, 1.72; 7-377)
1 Euxenite 97 (d 2.99, 3.66, 2.95; 9-442*)
5 *Hewettite* 236
6 *Kleinite* 32 (d 2.91, 2.62, 3.88; 2-0745), *mackayite* 177 (d 3.16, 1.61, 3.31; 7-405)
1 *Koppite* 90 (d 3.00, 1.83, 1.56; 2-0674)
6 *Mackayite* 177 (d 3.16, 1.61, 3.31; 7-405)
1 *Manganosite* 59 (d 2.22, 2.57, 1.57; 7-230)
7 *Melanotekite* 525
8 *Paralaurionite* 31
1 *Pyrrhite* 90
1 Samarskite 97 (d 2.98, 2.92, 3.13; 10-398*)
9 *Tellurite* 71 (d 3.26, 3.72, 3.01; 9-433)
10 Wolframite (hübnerite) 153 (d 3.00, 2.96, 3.78; 10-477)
1 *Yttrotantalite* 99
1 *Zirkelite* 90

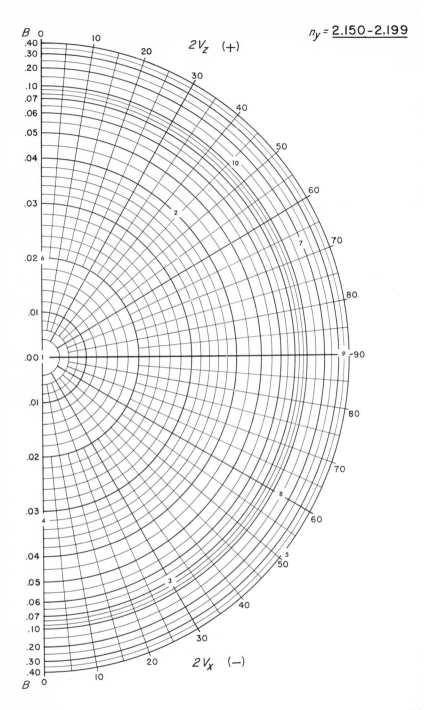

B 0

.40
.30
.20
.10
.07
.06
.05
.04
.03
.02 6
.01
.00 1

$2V_z$ (+)

n_y = <u>2.150-2.199</u>

10 20 30 40 50 60 70 80 9 -90

10 2 7

.01
.02
.03 4
.04
.05
.06
.07
.10
.20
.30
.40

B 0

80 70 8 60 5 50 40 3 30 20 10

$2V_x$ (−)

2.200–2.299

Isotropic
1 *Bunsenite* 59 (d 2.09, 2.41, 1.48; 4-0835)
1 Cerargyrite 26 (d 2.77, 1.96, 3.20; 6-0480)
1 *Eschynite* 97
1 *Lewisite* 235 (d 2.94, 1.81, 1.55; 7-66)
1 *Miersite* 26 (d 3.23, 2.28, 1.95; 2-0499)
1 *Polymignite* 100
1 Thorianite 65 (d 3.23, 1.69, 1.98; 4-0556)

Anisotropic and isotropic
2 *Alvarolite* [Florencio 1952, MA 12 305] (d 2.99, 3.69, 2.41; 7-58; = Mn-tantalite)
1 *Bunsenite* 59 (d 2.09, 2.41, 1.48; 4-0835)
1 Cerargyrite 26 (d 2.77, 1.96, 3.20; 6-0480)
3 Columbite-tantalite 95 (d 2.97, 3.66, 1.72; 7-64*)
4 *Cotunnite* 29 (d 3.58, 3.89, 2.78; 5-0418)
5 *Descloizite* 217
6 Endlichite 202
1 *Eschynite* 97
7 *Fervanite* 188
8 *Finnemanite* 236
9 *Iodyrite* 27 (d 3.75, 2.30, 3.98; 9-374)
10 *Kentrolite* 523
11 Lepidocrocite 76 (d 6.26, 3.29, 2.47; 8-98)
1 *Lewisite* 235 (d 2.94, 1.81, 1.55; 7-66)
12 Manganite 76 (d 3.40, 2.64, 2.28; 8-99*)
13 *Mendipite* 32 (d 3.09, 3.04, 2.78; 8-111)
1 *Miersite* 26 (d 3.23, 2.28, 1.95; 2-0499)
1 *Polymignite* 100
14 *Raspite* 153
15 *Stolzite* 148 (d 3.25, 2.02, 1.66; 8-476)
16 Tapiolite 94 (d 1.74, 3.33, 2.56; 8-181)
1 Thorianite 65 (d 3.23, 1.69, 1.98; 4-0556)
17 *Tripuhyite* 235 (d 3.28, 2.56, 1.72; 7-349)
18 Tungstite 72 (d 3.49, 2.68, 2.56; 6-0242)
19 *Vauquelinite* 179
20 Wolframite 153

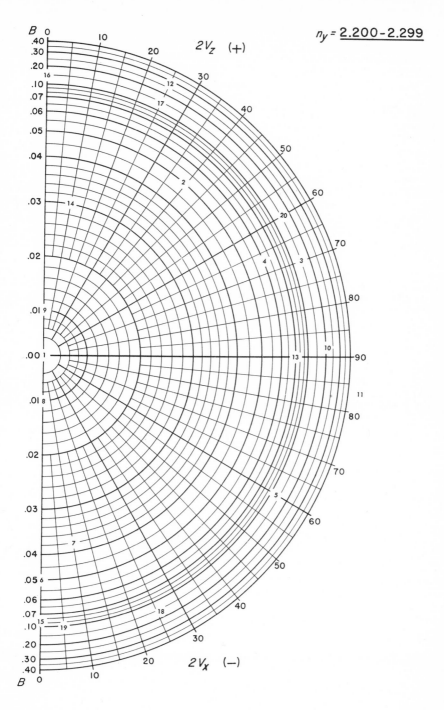

$n_y = \underline{2.200 - 2.299}$

B

$2V_z \quad (+)$

$2V_x \quad (-)$

Isotropic

1 *Brannerite* 95 (d 3.42, 1.90, 2.46; 8-2)
1 *Franklinite* 85 (d 2.55, 1.50, 2.99; 10-467)
1 *Jacobsite* 85 (d 2.56, 1.50, 3.01; 10-319)
1 *Magnesioferrite* 85 (d 2.53, 1.48, 1.61; 1-1114)
1 *Marshite* 26 (d 3.49, 2.14, 1.82; 6-0246)
1 *Nioboloparite* [Tikhonenkov 1957, MA 14 60]
1 Perovskite 91 (d 2.70, 1.91, 1.56; 9-365*)
1 Sphalerite 41 (d 3.12, 1.91, 1.63; 5-0566)
1 *Trevorite* 85 (d 2.51, 1.48, 1.61; 10-325)
1 *Wüstite* 58 (d 2.15, 2.49, 1.52; 6-0615)

Anisotropic and isotropic

2 *Brackebuschite* 189 (d 3.25, 4.95, 2.76; 6-0284)
1 Brannerite 95 (d 3.42, 1.90, 2.46; 8-2)
3 Columbite-tantalite 95 (d 2.97, 3.66, 1.72; 7-64*)
4 Crocoite 153 (d 3.28, 3.03, 3.48; 8-209*)
5 *Ecdemite* 236
1 *Franklinite* 85 (d 2.55, 1.50, 2.99; 10-467)
6 *Geikielite* 64 (d 2.72, 2.22, 2.53; 6-0494)
7 *Heterolite* 89 (d 2.46, 2.70, 1.52; 7-254)
8 *Hjelmite* 98
1 *Jacobsite* 85 (d 2.56, 1.50, 3.01; 10-319)
9 *Lângbanite* 529
10 *Lorettoite* 32
1 *Magnesioferrite* 85 (d 2.53, 1.48, 1.61; 1-1114)
1 *Marshite* 26 (d 3.49, 2.14, 1.82; 6-0246)
11 *Nadorite* 34
1 *Nioboloparite* [Tikhonenkov 1957, MA 14 60]
1 Perovskite 91 (d 2.70, 1.91, 1.56; 9-365)
12 *Phoenicochroite* 168
13 *Pseudobrookite* 91 (d 3.48, 2.75, 4.90; 9-182)
14 *Pyrobelonite* 218
15 *Schwartzembergite* 32
1 Sphalerite 41 (d 3.12, 1.91, 1.63; 5-0566)
1 *Trevorite* 85 (d 2.51, 1.48, 1.61; 10-325)
19 *U-Wulfenite* [Chernikov *et al.* 1960, MA 15 460]
16 *Valentinite* 64 (d 3.14, 1.80, 4.59; 3-0530)
17 Wolframite (ferberite) 153 (d 2.94, 1.71, 2.47; 10-449)
18 Wurtzite 43 (d 2.93, 3.31, 1.91; 10-434)
1 *Wüstite* 58 (d 2.15, 2.49, 1.52; 6-0615)
19 *U-Wulfenite* [Chernikov *et al.* 1960, MA 15 460]

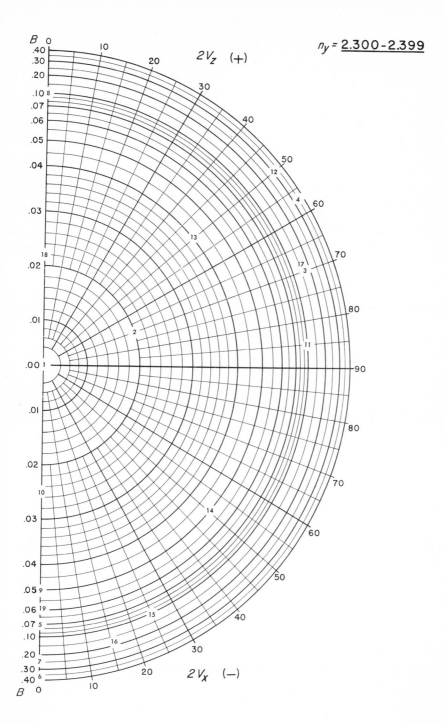

$n_y = \underline{\textbf{2.300-2.399}}$

$2V_z \ (+)$

$2V_x \ (-)$

B

Isotropic
1 *Cadmium oxide* 59 (d 2.71, 2.35, 1.66; 5-0640)
1 DIAMOND 20 (d 2.06, 1.26, 1.08; 6-0675)
1 *Eglestonite* 31 (d 3.16, 2.54, 1.95; 2-0547)
1 MAGNETITE 85 (d 2.53, 1.48, 2.97; 7-322)
1 *Sillenite* 60 (d 3.22, 1.74, 2.73; 6-0312)
1 SPHALERITE 41 (d 3.12, 1.91, 1.63; 5-0566)

Anisotropic and isotropic
1 *Cadmium oxide* 59 (d 2.71, 2.35, 1.66; 5-0640)
2 *Derbylite* 91
1 DIAMOND 20 (d 2.06, 1.26, 1.08; 6-0675)
1 *Eglestonite* 31 (d 3.16, 2.54, 1.95; 2-0547)
3 GOETHITE 79 (d 4.18, 2.44, 2.69; 3-0249
4 Hausmannite 88 (d 2.18, 2.14, 2.06; 5-0689), pyrophanite 64 (d 2.79, 2.58, 1.75; 2-0846)
1 MAGNETITE 85 (d 2.53, 1.48, 2.97; 7-322)
5 Minium 88 (B = −.006 to + .006) (d 3.38, 2.90, 2.79; 8-19)
4 Pyrophanite 64 (d 2.79, 2.58, 1.75; 2-0846)
1 *Sillenite* 60 (d 3.22, 1.74, 2.73; 6-0312)
1 SPHALERITE 41 (d 3.12, 1.91, 1.63; 5-0566)
6 Stibiotantalite 98 (d 3.15, 2.96, 1.89; 2-0552)
7 *Thoreaulite* 101
8 *Vanadinite* 202
9 Wulfenite 148 (d 2.94, 2.02, 1.65; 8-475)

74

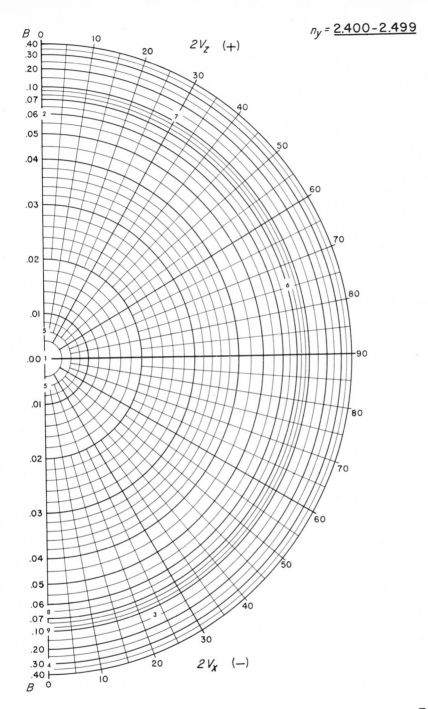

$n_y = \underline{2.400 - 2.499}$

$2V_z \quad (+)$

$2V_x \quad (-)$

>2.500
(n given in parentheses)

Isotropic
1 *Alabandite* (2.70) 41 (d 2.61, 1.85, 1.51; 6-0518)
1 Cuprite (2.849 red) 56 (d 2.47, 2.14, 1.51; 5-0667)
1 *Hauerite* (2.69) 49 (d 3.07, 1.18, 1.84; 10-476)
1 *Oxymagnite* (2.63 Li, av.) 85

Anisotropic and isotropic
1 *Alabandite* (2.70) 41 (d 2.61, 1.85, 1.51; 6-0518)
2 Anatase (2.561) 69 (d 3.51, 1.89, 2.38; 4-0477)
3 Brookite (2.584) 70 (d 3.47, 2.90, 1.38; 3-0380)
4 *Chalcophanite* (>2.72) 90 (d 6.88, 2.22, 2.45; 7-174)
5 Cinnabar (2.913) 45 (d 3.36, 2.86, 1.98; 6-0256)
1 Cuprite (2.849 red) 56 (d 2.47, 2.14, 1.51; 5-0667)
6 Enargite (3.089) 53 (d 3.22, 1.86, 2.87; 10-436)
7 *Greenockite* (2.506) 43 (d 3.16, 3.58, 3.36; 6-0314)
1 *Hauerite* (2.69) 49 (d 3.07, 1.18, 1.84; 10-476)
8 HEMATITE (3.22) 62 (d 2.69, 2.51, 1.69; 6-0502), proustite (3.088) 52 (d 2.76, 3.28, 3.18; 9-110)
9 *Hutchinsonite* (3.176) 54 (d 2.74, 3.78, 3.05; 8-124)
10 *Kermesite* (2.74) 47
11 *Lithargite* (2.665) 59 (d 3.12, 2.81, 1.87; 5-0561)
12 *Massicotite* (2.61) 59 (d 3.07, 2.95, 2.74; 5-0570)
13 *Moissanite* (2.6467) 20 (d 2.51, 2.63, 1.54; 4-0756*)
14 *Montroydite* (2.50) 60 (d 2.97, 2.83, 2.41; 9-381)
15 Orpiment (2.81) 47 (d 4.82, 2.70, 4.00; 1-0273)
1 *Oxymagnite* (2.63 Li, av.) 85
8 Proustite (3.088) 52 (d 2.76, 3.28, 3.18; 9-110)
16 *Pucherite* (2.50) 183
17 Pyrargyrite (3.084) 52 (d 2.81, 2.57, 3.22; 2-0835)
18 Realgar 2.684) 45 (d 5.40, 3.19, 2.94; 9-441)
19 RUTILE (2.612) 66 (d 3.25, 1.69, 2.49; 4-0551)
20 *Smithite* (3.27 ca.) 55
21 *Terlinguaite* (2.64) 32 (d 3.26, 2.51, 2.81; 2-0481)
22 *Xanthoconite* (3. ca.) 53 (d 3.00, 2.82, 3.14; 8-134)

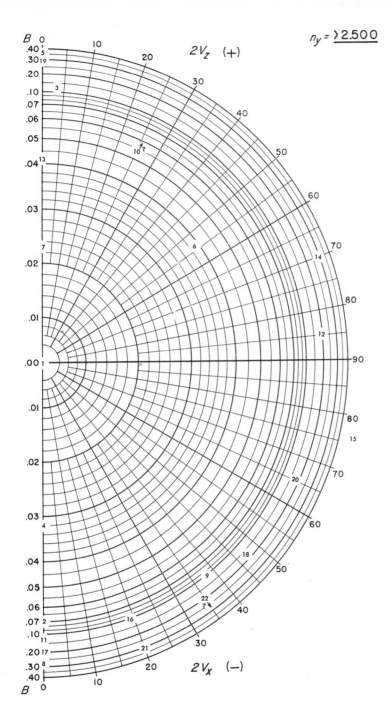

$n_y = \geq 2.500$

77

ALPHABETICAL INDEX OF MINERALS

80

82

Lopezite, 46
Lorettoite, 72
Loseyite, 38
Lossenite, 52
Lotrite, 40
Louderbackite, 28
Loughlinite, 24
Lovozerite, 30
Ludlamite, 40
Ludwigite, 56
Lueneburgite, 28

Mackayite, 68
Magnalumoxide, 48
Magnesiodolomite, 40
Magnesioferrite, 72
Magnesite, 44
Magnesium chalcanthite, 22
Magnesium orthite, 44
Magnetite, 74
Magniophilite, 44
Magniotriplite, 38
Magnussonite, 60
Malachite, 56
Malladrite, 16
Manandonite, 34
Manasseite, 26
Mangandolomite, 48
Manganite, 70
Manganolangbeinite, 30
Mangan-orthite (See Allanite, 52)
Manganosite, 68
Manganostibite, 60
Manganpyrosmalite, 40
Mansfieldite, 36
Margarite, 38
Margarosanite, 50
Marialite (See Scapolite, 28)
Marshite, 72
Mascagnite, 26
Massicotite, 76
Matlockite, 66
Mauritzite, 34
Meionite (See Scapolite, 34)
Melanocerite, 46
Melanotekite, 68
Melanovanadite, 60
Melanterite, 20
Melilite group, 36–40
Meliphanite, 34

Mellite, 26
Mendipite, 70
Mendozite, 18
Mercallite, 18
Merrillite, 36
Merwinite, 44
Mesolite, 24
Metahalloysite, 28
Metaheinrichite, 34
Metahewettite, 66
Metahohmanite, 44
Metaschoderite, 34
Metasideronatrite, 30
Metatorbernite, 36
Metatyuyamunite, 54
Metavariscite, 28
Metavauxite, 30
Metavoltine, 32
Metazeunerite, 32
Meyerhofferite, 26
Microcline, 26
Microlite, 64
Miersite, 70
Mikheevite, 30
Milarite, 26
Millisite, 32
Miloschite, 28
Mimetite, 66
Minasragrite, 26
Minguzzite, 28
Minium, 74
Minnesotaite, 34
Minyulite, 26
Mirabilite, 16
Misenite, 22
Mitscherlichite, 36
Mixite, 48
Mizzonite (See Scapolite, 32)
Mn-astrophyllite (See Kupletskite, 42)
Mn-tantalite (See Alvarolite, 70)
Moissanite, 76
Molybdophyllite, 54
Monazite, 52
Monetite, 34
Montanite, 64
Montgomeryite, 30
Monticellite, 38
Montmorillonite, 24–30
Montroydite, 76
Mooreite, 28

87